FROM CLIENT TO CLINICIAN

The Transformative Power of Neurofeedback Therapy
for Families Living with Autism and Other Special Needs

LOULOUA SMADI

Publishing services provided by 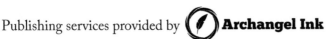 Archangel Ink

ISBN: 978-1-950043-27-9

To Milo and all the special souls–

Thank you for being you.

You are the gift that keeps on giving.

Contents

Acknowledgments and Permissions

This book testifies to how grateful I am for Dr. Lynette Louise and her work. My mentor and friend, she has taught me how to believe, dream, and live a life full of possibilities. I'm thankful for her trust, time, and patience in teaching me how to make a difference.

I have secured Lynette's permission to use excerpts from her acclaimed book *Miracles Are Made: A Real-Life Guide to Autism*. Her book was by my side at every step of my learning curve, offering an understandable and compelling explanation of neurofeedback while also presenting it in a familiar and loving context. I hope you find her excerpts as enlightening as I have.

A very special thank you to Dr. Reem Mouawad for her encouragement since day one and for her relentless advocacy for special needs people. She is a beacon of hope in Lebanon, a true inspiration.

I want to thank Dr. Ed Hamlin, whose admirable knowledge and support allowed me to take my first steps in the field. To Dr. Ainat Rogel, Regina Musicaro, and Dr. Bessel van der Kolk, whose guidance, time, and opportunities made all the difference in my growth.

I would like to show appreciation to Dr. Vincent Giampietro for giving me the chance to further my education and learn from the best, and Dr. Martijn Arns for his assistance and significant contribution to the field.

Thank you to the Archangel Ink team—Rob, Kristie, Paige, and Erica—for turning this manuscript into a book I am so incredibly proud of. The compassion you showed during my postpartum period and the August 4 explosions in Beirut will always stay in my heart.

Thank you to Sandy Draper for the beautiful editing that helped bring my words to life and for enabling me to be confident about this book's purpose.

I'm eternally grateful to all the clients, friends, and family I've worked with. Thank you for your trust.

To my mother, for setting an example and holding my hand at each step of the way.

To my father, for his guidance and unfaltering belief in me.

To my husband, Tarek, for his love, patience, and kindness; for the hours spent with me dreaming up this book; for making me a better person.

To my son, Talal, for giving life and love a whole new meaning.

To my sister and brother, Yasso and Nemo, for having each other's back no matter what.

To my sister-in-law, Tala, for her patience and craft in creating the best figures for this book.

To my best friend, Jiji, for constantly pushing me forward and cheering me on.

To my big sister, Sara, for always listening, crying, and laughing with me.

To May, for putting me on the path and healing my heart.

Thank you. You have all made me stronger, wiser, and prouder.

Balance is the secret of mental and physical health, and all life is endowed with the desire to achieve it. Sometimes we call that desire for balance: the pursuit of happiness.

–Dr. Lynette Louise, *Miracles Are Made: A Real-Life Guide to Autism*

Introduction

My Family's Journey to Neurofeedback

My journey with neurofeedback took place in the context of my family. The six of us were a fairly typical family except that one of my brothers, Ismail, known to us as Milo,[1] happened to fall on the autism spectrum.

Receiving Milo's diagnosis when he was two and a half years old, we faced the common struggles of anyone caring for a highly dependent autistic child. Milo was at first nonverbal and violent. Finding a therapist, doctor, or even a dentist to treat him wasn't easy. Like many children with autism spectrum disorder (ASD), Milo found school challenging, and the students and teachers didn't know how to behave around him. It was hard for us, too. We just wanted Milo to be "normal." Mom and Dad, in the most loving way possible, fretted about what would happen to Milo … tomorrow, next week, next month, next year. They were on a mission to find "a cure," waiting for a miracle to happen.

Today in 2020, at twenty-six, Milo lives in Tunisia and is working to earn a professional pastry chef certificate. He has grown more than we could have ever imagined, and we couldn't be prouder of him. But the best part? Milo is proud of himself.

What happened in the years in between? Our family explored various therapies, practitioners, and helpers to support Milo at each stage of his development, many of which you'll read about in this book.

---

1 Pronounced "Meelo" but written with an "I" because we speak French.

While each of these was a step along Milo's journey, some were more successful than others. Ultimately, neurofeedback and play therapy became the foundational approaches to helping Milo thrive. Dr. Lynette Louise, also known as The Brain Broad, an expert in autism, mental health, and neurofeedback, was instrumental in helping my brother flourish and in helping our family find hope and security.

Dr. Lynette Louise

While my parents and Milo always had the right intentions and drive, it was Dr. Lynette Louise who helped consolidate it all: her multifaceted approach supported Milo to continue to grow year after year.

Lynette taught us behavioral techniques to enhance Milo's progression, such as the power of play to teach him life skills. Neurofeedback therapy helped speed up Milo's learning considerably. Lynette also helped me, my parents, and my two other siblings with our respective challenges. As she demonstrated with my family, attending to other family member is as important as attending to the autistic child. In this way, they all help each other and reach new heights.

A mom of eight children—six of whom were adopted and four who were on the autism spectrum—Lynette's approach to healing stems from her family experience as well as her extensive experience with clients lower on the functioning spectrum of special needs. Her intelligence, intuition, and wittiness come from her healed sensory sensitivities and Asperger's syndrome (a high-functioning type of ASD).

I was taken by Lynette's approach, and I was drawn to neurofeedback therapy from the very start. I saw how it helped Milo calm down and be less violent, less sensory sensitive, and more social. And I saw firsthand how it helped my youngest brother's hyperactivity and inattention, my sister's sensory sensitivities and anxiety, and my depressive tendencies and inattention. In time, I was inspired to follow in Lynette's steps and train to become a neurofeedback clinician.

Neurofeedback

Neurofeedback, also called neurotherapy or electroencephalogram (EEG) biofeedback, is a non-intrusive brain-training technique providing moment-to-moment information on an individual's state of physiological functioning. Neurofeedback strengthens neuronal pathways as it brings about a functional reorganization in the brain toward balance by using informational feedback. A software reads and measures brain wave activity with an EEG by utilizing sensors placed on the scalp and amplifying that data in real time. We aim to normalize brain wave distribution and teach the brain by rewarding it with information through the use of a video game that provides auditory and visual rewards. Neurofeedback targets mood, energy levels, sleep quality, clarity, and sensory and cognitive processing. It can improve the symptoms of autism, attention deficit hyperactivity disorder (ADHD), learning disabilities, anxiety, depression, cerebral palsy, and many more disorders.

My personal journey from client to clinician was gripping. I feel blessed to have met and trained with many experts in the field, in addition to Lynette, and my learning was exponential. However, I never forgot my first and most personal experience with neurofeedback: that of the client. In time, I realized that my family's experience with Lynette was unparalleled. I found her approach better for the client, and her explanations about neurofeedback more compelling than any others I personally encountered. This inspired my professional journey, and following Lynette's approach to neurofeedback has brought me wonderful success with my clients.

Why I Wrote This Book

This book initially started as a tool to help me learn from Lynette while I was training with other neurofeedback experts. I wanted to learn more about Lynette's holistic approach, and since I couldn't travel into her clients' homes with her, I often reached out to her with questions. Those conversations eventually led to our collaboration in writing this book.

The manuscript accompanied me for six years and helped me make sense of the field's confusion, of my clinical worries, of Lynette's work, and of the healing journey as a whole. My professional training showed me that Lynette's clinical and personal experience with neurofeedback is unique. And after more than twelve years of working with her—from my fourteen-year-old self to today, as a clinician and mother—I feel it's crucial to bring forward her teachings by sharing our story.

I wrote this book in honor of how neurofeedback, and specifically Lynette's methods, helped my brother Milo and our family. I also wish to honor how they've helped me support other families as a clinician. Following this approach to neurofeedback has manifested beautiful changes in my clients.

Our message has also become increasingly important in the context of three problematic worldwide trends:

1. In the mental health and academic fields, the extensive use of diagnosis and medication has put emphasis on what is broken rather than on what is human.

2. With the rise of the wellness industry and social media, the pressures of attaining a certain norm and of teaching in an oversimplified way can be precarious.

3. The overreliance of technology in all fields has led to a failure in capturing human differences and including individualization.

In this context, I offer three lessons I hope you'll learn from this book.

1. The Value of Neurofeedback as a Tool

The first aim of this book is to inspire you to use neurofeedback. Neurofeedback is a tool to create something good on purpose. It is a tool for self-regulation that creates immediate change in a healthy manner. Most specifically, the aim is to acquaint you with Lynette's approach of using neurofeedback more holistically.

Unlike the field's approach of comparing the client's brain waves to a normative database, Lynette encourages us to follow clues in the client's emotional, behavioral, and cognitive responses, as these give us a window into how the client is operating. Her approach is centered on using the **arousal and compensatory lens**, on understanding the brain, and on using neuroanatomy as a guide. And, most importantly, Lynette uses neurofeedback by considering who the client wants to be. She asks the client, "How do you want to grow?" rather than "How can we get your brain to become normal like everyone else's?"

2. You Can't Fix Others, You Can Only Fix Yourself

The second important aim of this book is to communicate an essential component at the heart of Lynette's work: you can't fix others, you can only fix yourself. Whether through play, neurofeedback, or counseling, this is something Lynette taught and applied to my family. It's a fundamental truth I try to teach my clients too.

In the case of my family, we came to understand that the goal wasn't to fix Milo or to make him "normal," but to help him be happy, independent, ambitious, and self-sufficient. Trying to "fix" a loved one will never lead to real, long-lasting results because changing for someone else is not as powerful as changing for yourself. Moreover, looking at someone with the mindset of "fixing" them will only make your loved one feel broken and incomplete. Thus, the key is to empower them to want to fix themselves. The only way to create real and long-lasting change is by forging a path the client can follow to become who they want to be. If we help them find their motivation and reason to change, if we can help them help themselves, then their growth will be without end.

Nonetheless, while it is true that you can't fix someone else, the most critical part of this equation is that *you can fix yourself.* In fact, fixing yourself is the blueprint for it all. We must be observant of our mindset and beliefs and ensure they are aligned with our objectives. Fixing ourselves will only create better relationships and households. Being self-aware will give us more information about ourselves and the world. How can we help our loved ones flourish if we are not in a good place ourselves? How can we relate to their challenges if we don't first break down our own barriers?

3. How to Lead Your Life with Empathy

I wish to offer you what was delivered to my family: an alternative way of doing things, a way to say yes to empathy, friendship, and love. Like everyone else, we were given test results, a diagnosis, and a limited prognosis for Milo. But thanks to Lynette and neurofeedback, we were able to focus on healing and wellness rather than diagnosis and illness.

We hope to inspire you to be empathetic and to see things from another person's perspective. Because empathy allows the truth to blossom. We aim to create change in this world by inspiring people toward independence and ambition, by being empathetic to what that means for them.

Using This Book

Whether you are a parent, caregiver, therapist, or potential client, I trust this book will offer you an account of using neurofeedback that is personal, realistic, and inspired by love.

This is the story of my neurofeedback journey from client to clinician under the guidance of Dr. Louise, whom I refer to as Lynette throughout this book, as she is both a friend and a mentor. My brother Ismail (Milo) has been my inspiration since day one. Because my story would be incomplete without his, I've used both of our journeys to retrace the past and include everything we've learned along the way.

My story from client to clinician illustrates different approaches to healing using neurofeedback. I particularly showcase the strong discrepancies between the research and clinical worlds, as well as Lynette's unique approach using the arousal and compensatory lens and neuroanatomy as a guide.

I share personal and family stories to illustrate the paths Milo and I took. I share excerpts from Lynette's book *Miracles Are Made: A Real-Life Guide to Autism* that has helped me understand neurofeedback further. I also share recollections from my personal conversations with Lynette that helped clear up my confusion with the field. My intention behind comparing Lynette's approach to the rest of the field is not to show disapproval of the field but to support a methodology that I have found consistent success with.

This book won't teach you how to practice neurofeedback per se, but it will show its potential and illustrate how you can use neurofeedback more holistically thanks to Lynette's approach. In the Recommended Reading section at the end of the book, I refer you to essential books that offer a more comprehensive history and a technical and practical explanation of neurofeedback. I did not want to replicate what has been done so well already or digress from our main message and story.

Finally, I hope you will find this book useful in integrating neurofeedback or the arousal and compensatory lens within your own practice, living, and thinking. The offered methodology is merely a guide and should be an extension of your own toolbox of solutions. We are the first to understand that results will come from a hybrid of techniques that were adapted to you specifically. You should be encouraged to have the freedom to think outside the box and to keep learning from all sources.

Healing is a fluid work in progress, just as our approach is. In the same way Lynette has innovated, and then I have innovated, it is now up to you to make it your own. Only you know what works best for you.

Milo doing neurofeedback, Paris, 2014

My brother Milo and me, France, 2015

PART I

INSPIRATION

The effectiveness of neurofeedback lies in its interdisciplinary approach. It is a self-regulation tool that aims to balance your brain's electrical activity to help you open up to the possibilities of life. Neurofeedback can help you to become who you want to be.

Part I recounts stories of Milo and me as we made progress in our work with Lynette and the pivotal role neurofeedback played in helping us heal. We will explore how Milo stopped being self-abusive and how I stopped feeling inattentive and down. We will discuss the lessons learned and how they inspired me to pursue a career in neurofeedback. We will also delve into what neurofeedback is and how it can help us heal.

CHAPTER 1

A Nonlinear Miracle

The contrast between my brother's nerves and the calmness of the mosque was palpable. It wasn't so much that Milo had a meltdown during prayer, but that the setting was so serene compared to his emotional state. Milo was fifteen at the time, and puberty had hit him hard. We had been doing neurofeedback for two years and were in the middle of a behavioral therapy program. We had already seen significant improvements, but he was still struggling—especially with inconsolable emotional outbursts.

It was summer, and we were visiting our family roots in Damascus, Syria. That day the six of us headed into the Souk Al Hamidiyeh to explore Old Damascus, and as we approached the end of the covered market, the Umayyad Mosque—one of the largest and oldest mosques in the world—came into sight. Today this sacred place lies in ruins because of the Syrian Civil War, but when we visited, it was still an untouched gem.

As we entered, we were awed by the large, open courtyard and the spacious, column-filled prayer hall. Although the weather was hot and humid, and the mosque was bustling with life, I sensed its sacredness. Feeling like a foreigner, I was a bit intimidated by the crowds. As time went on, though, I realized we probably all shared the same questions and hopes. But then I saw Milo. He was standing in the middle of the prayer room, slamming the back of his hand against his nose, teeth, and mouth. From past experience, we knew if he continued, he might hurt himself or even lash out at someone trying to help him.

Mom and Dad went to calm him, but it was too late: Milo was already panicking and bleeding profusely from his nose due to the damaged blood vessels. My parents knew the only solution was to leave. Milo didn't agree; he didn't want to spoil our time. His screams echoed through the mosque as we made our exit. Many people tried to help us, offering tissues, water, and advice. They walked with us to make sure we were all right. While we appreciated their kindness, the fear, embarrassment, and helplessness we felt were traumatizing.

This story illustrates Milo's general state at that time—tense and nervous—but also our family struggles. Milo's anxiety created heightened tension for his family and for the bystanders at the mosque, and it wasn't conducive to helping him calm down.

As I said earlier, Milo was right in the middle of his neurofeedback training, so you might be surprised when I say that this story reminds me of how far Milo had come at this point. Even though Milo had a massive meltdown that day, the intensity and frequency of his outbursts had already improved. What I'd like you to take from this story is that therapy, *any therapy*, will never provide linear miracle progress. There will always be a difference between the outset and the present, which is why remembering the past is crucial: it reminds us of the growth achieved so far and inspires us to strive forward, to raise the bar.

Milo has always been determined, ever since he was a little boy. He showed persistence in any activity he undertook, although it often looked like the opposite because he lacks a sense of urgency. My brother is a driven and strong-willed man, and he deserves all the credit for his progress. He is kind and loving, convicted and courageous.

Ismail was also lucky to have a younger sister and brother, Yasmine and Namir, who have always accepted him and treated him with the utmost respect. Yasmine's support of Milo was evident in her calmness and desire to help no matter the circumstances, although she felt that her support was rarely encouraged or wanted. Her sweetness and attention to each one of us made our family dynamics smooth and effortless. Namir never uttered a complaint about Milo and always encouraged him to get out of his comfort zone, although he's had his fair share of embarrassment and annoyance with him. His way of taking care of his big brother while simultaneously showing him honor and dignity is beautiful to witness.

However, the full credit and admiration goes to my parents. They championed us, supported us, and loved us unceasingly. Our dad has always believed in Milo, seeing him as a boy full of endless possibilities. His faith and trust in Milo opened many doors for him. Without exception, he included Milo in all our family outings and refused to go anywhere without him. Afraid for his son's uncertain future, Dad always pushed Milo further. Although this widened his comfort zone over time, it often created tension between them. Our mom is a ray of angelic sunshine and our family's unfailing rock. She truly loves and accepts Milo for who he is and has taken care of him like a proper mama bear, although she experienced constant anguish and anxiety, afraid of not knowing what to do with him. She has learned when to let go of him. To me, this is the true proof of her love.

Above all, my parents were smart enough to surround themselves with the right people and the right tools. They credit Lynette with teaching them the importance of constantly raising the bar for Milo. This fearless approach allowed him to succeed.

A Different Type of Therapist

Lynette offered us a different definition of the word *therapist* or *clinician*. She travels around the world and works on-site in her clients' homes with their families. During her five-day visit, she uses a combination of play therapy, family dynamics counseling, and neurofeedback to help adults and children alike. Clients usually purchase their own neurofeedback software approved by Lynette before her arrival so they can continue the work after she leaves. She thus teaches the caregivers the basic neurofeedback skills necessary and then guides all her clients online while they continue the sessions themselves. She often makes return visits to the family.

While her home model made the experience comfortable for my family, it was her loving attitude toward us that made therapy especially appealing. She is a mother in her heart and a friend to all of us, including Milo. While helping my brother heal, she made sure the process was pleasant for all and made it clear how important a strong family is for healing.

Lynette's ability to combine her beliefs with her extensive collection of tools is what makes her one of a kind. Believing in healing, looking at someone holistically, prioritizing happiness, and landing on love is always at the top of her agenda while using biofeedback to create the most change possible. As explained by the Association for Applied Psychophysiology and Biofeedback (AAPB), "Biofeedback is a process that enables an individual to learn how to change physiological activity to improve health and performance."[2] Lynette's use of neurofeedback (biofeedback for the brain) coupled with her play therapy program adapted from biofeedback brings her healing power to the next level.

Having witnessed her work with my brother, my family, and me, I was fascinated by neurofeedback from the very start. I was impressed by the changes in Milo, as I observed him become more independent, calmer, happier, and more social. And I was amazed at the changes in myself: I became happier and more clear-headed and focused. I was also fascinated by the science behind neurofeedback and by Lynette's smooth clinical application. But my interest in the subject solidified when I read some of Lynette's case studies in her book

2   "About Biofeedback," AAPB.org, accessed December 1, 2020, https://www.aapb .org/i4a/pages/index.cfm?pageid=3463.

Miracles Are Made: A Real-Life Guide to Autism. They showcase her thinking behind each solution and are worth sharing here.[3]

One of my autistic clients was showing signs of auditory schizophrenia, so given that hearing voices is often accompanied (correlation noted, no causation known) by too much dopamine in the right temporal lobe, I decided to discourage stimulation in this area. I used a low-frequency reward and placed the sensor just above the right ear. After around ten sessions, he stopped listening to the sounds of ghosts as his imaginary voices quieted to a whisper and then went away.

A young girl I worked with was a chronic liar. I read that lying activates the anterior cingulate, which, when underactive, is often complicit in ADHD (Attention Deficit Hyperactivity Disorder). Given that many ADHD children tend toward telling lies (possibly self-medicating through behavior?) and that she had some of the ADHD symptoms, trying to stimulate the anterior cingulate through the use of an fpz placement (front middle of forehead) and encouraging activation with a high-frequency reward made sense. I accompanied this therapy with some "how to get out of the grave you just dug yourself into" approaches like "When you catch yourself lying, make it part of your sense of humor to embellish a story and then admit—'Yeah! That's a lie,' and then laugh." She became known for her unpredictable sense of humor and outrageous stories. So, though she still lied, she did it with flair and with thoughtful preparation rather than uninhibited desperation. And as a side-benefit her grades improved....

I worked with a young man who loved music so much he would get stuck in it. Whenever this happened I would brighten his left frontal lobe to diminish the hold his right temporal lobe had over

---

3   Lynette Louise, *Miracles Are Made: A Real-Life Guide to Autism* (Bandon: Robert Reed Publishers, 2011), 198–200.

him… after a few sessions, he would get too into numbers and become too manically happy so we would treat the right temporal lobe to calm down the effect of the left frontal lobe. This seesawing approach went on for months until he reached a point where he was cooperating, answering questions, and showing spontaneous affection. Interesting to note that his affection wasn't always welcomed because it went through a phase of inappropriate behavior. This was a challenge for the family, and although the problem is common with autism, they read his new touches as a dire indication of possible past indiscretions. They began to look for culprits. It was a responsible reaction, but it did waylay them from continuing his therapy for a time while they dug at family skeletons. Fortunately, they found their way back. We treated his right temporal lobe and completed the job of getting to their goal: integration.

Since I read that focus is controlled by the left frontal area as well as the right parietal, I began using a combination with many extremely focus-challenged children, doing half the session in the back right and the other half in the left front. This has become one of my favorite protocols for many children with autism—one boy even looked at me midway through this low-frequency calming of the right parietal lobe and said, "I'm getting that happy Ritalin feeling." But even though he said that, when I treated him only on the right parietal lobe, he became depressed. It was the combo that really worked to help him be social and happy.

These explanations reveal Lynette's comprehensive understanding and smooth application, which I have always found inspiring. Families and clinicians around the world all refer to Lynette's touch as the "Lynette effect." I hope you can glean the essence of it through those examples. The first time I read them, they painted a picture of what was possible, which encouraged me to seek out my own experience.

CHAPTER 2

Learning Together as a Family

M ilo was diagnosed with autism when he was two and a half years old—nowadays, this is considered late, as it usually happens at eighteen months. ASD is a developmental disorder characterized by impairments in communication, language, and social interaction combined with repetitive and restricted behaviors. While my brother spoke five words ("up," "Dad," "Mom," "bye," "no") by the time he was a year old, thus indicating normal cognitive development, six months later his language and eye contact completely disappeared. Milo also started to withdraw and was obsessed with animals and numbers, but little else.

Our handsome blue-eyed boy struggled with communication and sensory integration issues, characteristic of ASD. He was nonverbal and had many self-stimulatory behaviors, also known as "stims" (short for stimulation). Milo's stims included making loud noises, tapping his mouth with the back of his hands, tapping the front of his pants on his private parts while looking very closely at one detailed area on the wall, closing his ears, jumping in the air, and, my favorite, running around while screaming and tapping his face all at once.

Stims (also sometimes known as "isms," a suffix to indicate addiction to the movement) are defined as repetitive body movements, words, or actions, and have been understood as ways for individuals with ASD to block sensory overload, regulate emotions, and/or relieve anxieties. While Milo's stims were generally harmless, situations became more complicated when those sensory issues combined with whatever was troubling him, his inability to communicate, or our inability to understand him. They would then turn into full-on tantrums (an outburst caused by someone or something) or meltdowns (generally due to sensory overwhelm).

As soon as Milo was diagnosed, my parents' objective was to make Milo as "normal" as possible. Back in 1998, there was limited knowledge about autism, especially in France, which meant my parents didn't know how to help him for the best, and there was inadequate support from doctors, schools, and therapists. Milo couldn't speak or comprehend words being spoken to him, which was challenging and frustrating for my parents. Thus, the most pressing goal was to teach him how to talk and how to understand what others said to him.

Learning to Talk and Understand

With this objective in mind, my parents were first referred to a child psychiatrist, who essentially spent her time merely observing Milo from afar. When there were no signs of progress, my father went looking for an educational therapist and finally found Madame Eliane Chaulet, who agreed to work on Milo's communication and motor skills. Madame Chaulet had developed a particular educational and therapeutic method for children with special needs that entailed Milo learning how to read before talking. While this sounded impossible to my parents at the time, her approach was key to developing Milo's communication skills.

She first started with his motor rehabilitation, focusing on his body and hand (gross motor) movements to strengthen his brain-body connection and to eventually help with his writing (fine motor movements). Her work was based on repetition, as she believed this was necessary for learning. She then started to teach him how to read using a method called "La méthode Borel-Maisonny," in which each phonetic sound had an associated gesture.

When Milo wasn't with Madame Chaulet, he attended the same primary school as me. Knowing that I'm only eighteen months older than him, you can only imagine the number of embarrassing stories I collected. At the time, children like Milo didn't have many options other than regular school (as opposed to the special needs environment that is common today), and the school's knowledge of autism was limited. Since Milo wasn't able to talk, he was generally aggressive and unhappy there and used to bite his classmates. He loved to ring the school fire alarm, which would then disrupt the entire school. And even when the school tried to discipline him, it didn't stop my brother. Once, while standing outside the principal's office awaiting punishment, he needed to pee. But he couldn't speak and ask to go to the toilet, so he thought it was a good idea to pee in the flowerpot. Clearly, being misunderstood was Milo's life theme song.

Through school and therapy with Madame Chaulet, we were both growing and, thankfully, Milo was improving. Madame Chaulet's work centered on associating Milo's visual and auditory pathways, and thus Milo first learned syllables, consonants, and vowels, which then eventually built up into full words. At this point, my parents knew that if they wanted Milo to stay in a regular school, he'd need more help, so they hired a special needs assistant, Tatiana, to support him. Tatiana played an integral part in helping Milo become comfortable at school. His reading improved; he learned to pronounce words correctly, to read aloud, and to write. Milo's speech still only consisted of a few words, but these words had meaning to Milo; thus, he started to understand other people's words. Making sentences was challenging, and he struggled to conjugate and integrate verbs. However, talking helped my brother calm down a little as he realized that others would listen when he asked for what he needed, like "toilet," "water," or "food."

Milo wasn't the only one seeing Madame Chaulet. I also worked with her on my struggles with speech. Being Lebanese, my parents spoke to me in English and Arabic, and I was accustomed to English-speaking media only. However, when I entered a French kindergarten, I had to switch to speaking French, and by the time we were teaching Milo how to talk, our rule at home was to only speak French. My confusion between English, French, and Arabic led to learning difficulties, and I developed a small lisp where my /s/ and /z/ sounded like "th." Madame Chaulet helped me with my French grammar, conjugation, and vocabulary, and I saw a speech therapist to help me with my pronunciation. I remember the sessions with Madame Chaulet being tedious and tiring, but fruitful. You could say that working with Madame Chaulet first inspired my fascination with human development and healing.

It's important to add that while we were focused on Milo's communication, my parents also did their best to integrate and entertain him as much as possible. My father was absent half of the time traveling for work, so he was determined to take Milo out and teach him everything he could whenever he was home with us. Dad took us to the zoo and Disneyland often because of how much Milo loved animals and Disney characters, and he took us to museums in order to teach him art, culture, and science. We went horseback riding and took jujitsu classes together because my parents read the practices would support Milo's learning and motricity. My dad taught Milo how to swim and ride a bike—fun activities we love to do as a family to this day. However, these activities were challenging, especially if Milo had a meltdown. This left my parents arguing most of the time: Mom wished Dad could be more sensitive to Milo's emotional state, while Dad wished Mom could be braver when it came to his learning.

A New Approach

Over the next few years, Milo and I worked on our difficulties side by side. Milo continued to improve in his reading, writing, and speech, and I continued to improve in my French. After six years of hard work with Madame Chaulet and at school, ten-year-old Milo could read flawlessly and never made a spelling mistake; his handwriting was scribbly but correct; he could pronounce any word but struggled with grammar, verbs, and syntax; and he could understand the basic meaning of others' statements, commands, and questions. Thanks to Madame Chaulet, Milo had reached new heights.

While Milo's changes sound beautiful, the path he walked to achieve them was a rocky one. Madame Chaulet's approach was earnest, directive, and strict (slapping him was part of the package). Her style only focused on Milo's learning disabilities and had nothing to do with social skills or his personal happiness. Eventually, after those six years, Milo became robotic and compliant. He ate when he was told to eat. He dressed when he was told to dress. He didn't smile anymore and didn't express his feelings. He would have meltdowns from time to time, but no one understood why, and no one bothered to ask why. Mom felt like her happy boy had been replaced by a sad robot who had meltdowns. It didn't matter if he liked something or not, if he didn't want to do something or not—he had learned to be compliant, and we had learned to make him do what we wanted. While my parents were grateful for Milo's academic progress, they were very fearful about the future. They had no direction or aspirations for him. And while he had learned those communication skills, my brother had now become so closed off that there wasn't even an opportunity, time, or place for him to use them.

Even when we were out doing the activities Milo supposedly had an interest in, he didn't seem to enjoy them. His interactions with us didn't improve, and the therapy had failed to teach him to share his thoughts and emotions. Milo was mostly concerned about pleasing my parents and not upsetting them. He didn't care about pleasing himself. In truth, my parents hated his autistic behaviors, and this led to lots of angry shouting and punishing.

My parents finally realized things had to change. At the same time, Milo was entering the fifth grade and was "asked to leave" by the school's new principal, who didn't embrace the challenge of having Milo in her establishment. My parents decided to homeschool him (as Dad believed Milo was bright and intelligent), and Mom started researching the different behavioral therapies that were available. Applied behavior analysis (ABA), which focuses on eliminating unwanted behaviors and encouraging wanted behaviors through repetition and reward, was the most prevalent at that time. However, Mom had had a taste of this with Madame Chaulet and was tired of this approach. She wanted more for Milo.

Acceptance

The turning point came in 2005 when my parents were referred to The Son-Rise Program®, a behavioral therapy program taught by the Autism Treatment Center of America®. Until this point, we treated Milo like any other child and expected him to behave accordingly because making him "normal" was our only goal. My father was the first to go to one of their training sessions, and he was immediately convinced by their accepting approach. He called my mom and instructed her to empty our living room in order to make space for Milo's new playroom. My parents immediately implemented a program designed around Milo; we would no longer expect him to fit in within our family norms.

The Son-Rise Program® is an alternative treatment for autism that understands the disorder to be social-relational instead of behavioral. It teaches parents all over the world to create home-based, child-centered programs to reach the child. They believe we need to join the child's world first, instead of forcing them to conform to ours, and use play as a tool to connect with the children. More than changing our strategies, the program changed our beliefs; it encouraged and taught us how to love Milo's autism and to love Milo for who he is. Thanks to this program, autism became the most loving and funniest element in our family, and we made it our goal to see Milo happy, independent, and self-sufficient. We learned to giggle when we watched people on the street react to Milo's unusual sounds and movements instead of fearing their judgment. Instead of trying to stop Milo's autistic behaviors, we learned to accept them.

The Son-Rise Program® didn't change Milo as much as it changed my parents. It essentially taught them 1) the power of choosing to be happy at any moment in your life, 2) the importance of being nonjudgmental toward others and ourselves, and 3) the significance of rewiring one's beliefs, as they have a direct result on one's actions and behaviors. This approach made my parents feel like they could finally catch a break. It was a relief not to continually hear what was wrong with their son, but rather to be taught to love and accept him. It helped my parents feel less guilty and overwhelmed in the present and become more relaxed about the future. When they changed for Milo, they changed for the rest of us as well.

My parents modified what they learned from the program, implementing a program customized to Milo's capabilities, as they believed he was curious and capable enough to do more than what the standard program offered. In this way, Mom and Dad set out to create a world perfectly suited for Milo to blossom.

From that point on, Milo's days were divided into two parts. His mornings consisted of two to three hours of homeschooling one-on-one. He had the most incredible, kind, patient, and understanding professors teaching him French and mathematics. Mom was responsible for teaching him English, which, contrary to belief, became useful for him in terms of understanding the meaning of words more profoundly. Milo's afternoons were then filled with two-hour play therapy sessions, inspired by The Son-Rise Program®, with different volunteers recruited from the American University of Paris. Those helper friends, as we called them, were generally interested in psychology and wanted experience working with students with special needs.

At first, the play sessions were conducted exclusively in my brother's playroom. We had many wonderful helper friends who engaged in various games with Milo. The objectives were always to socialize, to reinforce his language, and to keep interactions and eye contact going for as long as possible. Seeing all of my brother's lovely helper friends making my brother better brought warmth to my fifteen-year-old heart, afflicted as I was with the angst of teen life.

Thanks to this change, my family learned to choose happiness rather than living in survival mode. We learned to go at Milo's pace and to act out his stims to show acceptance. We understood that Milo engaged in self-stimulating behaviors in order to make himself feel better, the same way we all find forms of self-soothing. When he tapped his face, we tapped ours; when he jumped in the air, so did we. We learned about his interests and engaged in the activities he enjoyed. As we loved him fully, he became calmer and more willing to open up to us.

An example that illustrates this change would be how we responded to Milo's love for classical music. For the previous three years, Milo had had a growing obsession with classical music, which meant he didn't want to do anything but listen to his music. Not knowing what to do and wanting to fit him into the "norm," my parents only allowed Milo to listen to music on Saturdays. After implementing what we learned from the program, we embraced his interests and used them as motivation for learning and social interaction. Thus, we started listening to music with him and made games out of his favorite musical piece of all time, "Pierre et le Loup" by Prokofiev. Milo's love for music was one of my favorite things about him, as that was one of the few things we had in common. Although his interest in classical music eventually disappeared, his love for beats and melodies of all genres remains.

As a result, he finally began to trust us, and we started to notice a change in him. For example, air travel used to be challenging for Milo, but he learned to find his calm by writing lists of animals or Disney characters with my mom. Milo also learned to express himself and realize what he wanted and when he wanted it. He learned to say no to us, and we respected it. We didn't make him go to musical shows or restaurants with us anymore, and he was happy. Instead of stopping Milo, we would find a way to help him deal with whatever was going on. Milo became a person, an entity. We let him have a choice. We let him have preferences. He unfolded as a young man, and we got to know him. Another positive result was that his social interactions improved, he relaxed, and he was more able to learn.

Physiological Help

It is crucial to put things into context and take into account the complexity of autism. Milo improved—but *relative to* how he used to be. On the one hand, Milo had relaxed in terms of his identity and his relationship toward others, and he had learned to properly communicate with his loved ones. On the other hand, Milo was entering his puberty years, and his tantrums and meltdowns were getting worse by the day. This dichotomy of improvement and struggle is what makes autism such a complex disorder. One second we were grateful for Milo's changes, and the next, we were completely desperate.

Milo's typical outburst consisted of crying, slamming his hand against his head, and knocking his chin and teeth against the back of his hand, which would lead to bleeding. When the pain eventually made him stop, he would resort to hitting the shoulder of the person next to him with his chin and teeth. The causes of Milo's meltdowns were often a mystery to us. We understood they were generally due to a combination of sensory overload and frustration toward us, but we were still powerless to help him. At times, Milo would throw a tantrum when there was something he didn't want to do; not knowing any better, my family would give in and allow him whatever he wanted. Other times, he would have a meltdown out of the blue as a way to self-soothe. Over the years, Milo came to understand the power of his tantrums on others and himself.

It was painful for us to watch Milo wound himself this way. Standing there, not knowing how to help, was painful; being the object of his abuse (he would hit our arms, shoulders, or heads with his chin and teeth) was painful too. The Son-Rise Program® taught us how to understand Milo and showed us how to offer him ways to cope: we let him stay home when he felt too sensitive or unable to socialize, we found ways to help him calm down afterward, and we tried to shift behavior before a meltdown occurred. No matter what we did, though, Milo continued to have four to six tantrums a day. His violence frightened us, and while our strategies were helping his behavior, it seemed like Milo was always physiologically unwell.

During this time, Milo's meltdowns were happening so frequently that we avoided taking him places, and his learning with his helper friends was often interrupted by a tantrum. My parents' only objective became to stop Milo's tantrums and meltdowns. We needed new tools to help Milo maintain a calm disposition and to help him feel better. My parents had tried many other therapies, including EFT Tapping,[4] the DAN! Protocol with nutritional therapy,[5] Nambudripad's Allergy Elimination Technique,[6] and many others—but none created significant improvements for Milo. My parents were left feeling hopeless. This was when we were referred to Lynette and neurofeedback by our Son-Rise Program® coordinator. Dr. Lynette Louise was their last hope; they were desperate.

---

4   Emotional Freedom Techniques (EFT) is an alternative treatment used to manage physical pain and emotional distress.

5   The DAN! Protocol, known for its biomedical interventions such as chelation and hyperbaric oxygen treatment, has been discontinued.

6   Nambudripad's Allergy Elimination Technique (NAET) consists of a combination of kinesiology and acupressure.

Enter Dr. Lynette Louise

After a couple months of researching neurofeedback, a novel therapy my parents had never before heard of, they hired Lynette for an in-home outreach in June 2007 when Milo had just turned thirteen. When Lynette arrived, she asked my parents to clarify their main reason for hiring her. She wanted to know what change they were looking for. They made it clear they wanted help with Milo's meltdowns and tantrums. With this in mind, Lynette went to play with Milo in his playroom. She explained that it was vital for her to get to know Milo, his personality, his behavior, and how his brain functioned.

Lynette's play and attitude with Milo were different from any other therapist my parents had encountered so far. They saw her study his brain and behavior, pushing him left and right to understand his capabilities and limits. But what touched them most was how she embraced him and loved him in every act; she treated him as her equal and her friend.

Helping Milo to feel comfortable with the gels and cleaners needed for neurofeedback, as well as the wires, took extraordinary talent. To an outsider, it would appear that Milo had no trouble being compliant and staying seated, but we knew better; Lynette was a natural at gaining Milo's trust.

After several neurofeedback sessions with Milo, Lynette reported that my brother's EEG was showing too little movement in the back of his brain. Lynette said we needed to train Milo with neurofeedback to make more brain wave activity at low frequencies in the back of the brain and less in the front—which she presumed was the reason for his anger and stims. He also had a lot of movement in the right temporal lobe and too few low frequencies in the central strip of his brain, which could explain why he fought his sleep so much. She reported that Milo had more right-hemisphere issues, which is common in patients with autism. She explained that they often have high amplitude of high-frequency brain wave activity in the back of the brain, and high amplitude of low-frequency brain wave activity in the front. The opposite is true for non-autistic individuals. Milo's left hemisphere had been working better than his right hemisphere, and he had lots of high-frequency brain activity in the front. Lynette also explained that due to the low brain wave activity in the back, Milo would be less focused at times—which would lead his brain to compensate with anxiety. He would feel anxious to compensate for the low waves; to compensate for his anxiety, he would try to balance his state by moving his body or getting nervous or screaming at someone.

Hearing an explanation of what was happening in Milo's brain finally allowed my parents to understand how Milo's physiology led him to behave in certain ways. Lynette said there was a lot to do but that we would help him by calming his overall fear and his perseverative frontal thinking by rewarding slower waves in the right temporal lobe.

Within her first week, Lynette's behavioral approach, along with neurofeedback, convinced my parents that continuing with neurofeedback would be worthwhile. Although it was obviously overwhelming, Mom and Dad came to quickly understand the efficacy of neurofeedback in calming my brother. My parents bought their own neurofeedback system, and Lynette took the time to teach my mom the basics of neurofeedback so they could keep doing good work even when Lynette had gone.

During her visit, Lynette assesses every family member's brain, does individualized neurofeedback on each family member, and teaches the basic neurofeedback skills necessary to continue without her. She also teaches behavioral techniques to enhance the results and counsels on family dynamics to improve relationships. Once she leaves, she guides all her clients online while they continue the sessions themselves and oftentimes comes back for returned visits to the family.

Lynette deems that working at home with her clients (and particularly special needs individuals) is more beneficial as they are generally more comfortable at home than in a clinic. Most children present differently at the clinic than at home or school, and this isn't useful from a neurofeedback or behavioral point of view. At the clinic, the child's brain cues to the newness and is obligated to adapt and cope. The real issues and anxieties emerge at home. If we measure the child's brain at home, we measure their general brain states, which will enable us to help them even more.

Lynette believes that the real, deep work is done in familiar surroundings and also needs to be done with and to the entire family. In this way, the parents or caregiver and therapist have the power to bring consistent and holistic long-term change. She thus pushes parents to acquire the knowledge they need to take care of their child and to claim the power to do so. She prefers to treat the whole family since, generally, it is common to find brain dysfunctions within a group of relatives. Lynette's model is built on the belief that people who help themselves will be better at helping other people.

While other therapists might disagree, Lynette has found success in teaching parents to become the leader in healing under the therapist's supervision. Putting the healing in the hands of the parents or caregivers makes sense because they are the ones who have to deal with all the difficult moments, and it saves having to schedule an appointment at the clinic when the upset is over. Hence, it became clear to Lynette that teaching the brain how to rewire and fire comfortably when someone is in an uncomfortable state is more beneficial in the long run. And being able to offer a tool to your child in need is more empowering than feeling helpless, constantly asking, "What now? When does the clinic open?!"

TAKEAWAYS

❖ ASD is a developmental disorder characterized by impairments in communication, language, and social interaction and often manifests repetitive and restricted behaviors. Stims are defined as repetitive body movements, words, or actions that allow individuals with ASD to block sensory overload, regulate emotions, and/or relieve anxieties.

❖ The Son-Rise Program®, an alternative treatment for autism that understands the disorder to be social-relational instead of behavioral, made us realize that the goal wasn't to make Milo "normal" but to make him happy, independent, and self-sufficient. We learned to understand him, respect him and his pace, love him and his autism, and choose happiness. In turn, he began to trust us and to express himself; he relaxed and was more able to learn.

❖ Lynette works all over the world in her clients' homes with their families. She finds that working in homes rather than clinics is more beneficial because:

  ◦ Clients are generally more comfortable at home.

  ◦ Children present differently at the clinic because they have to adapt to and cope with a new setting.

  ◦ The real issues and anxieties usually arise at home.

  ◦ Good work is done to the entire family: people who help themselves will be better at helping other people function better.

  ◦ Putting the healing in the hands of the parents or caregivers is empowering because they are the ones who have to deal with the difficult moments.

CHAPTER 3

Discovering Neurofeedback

It took time, patience, and an open mind to fully understand Lynette's ways. Her uniqueness can be intimidating at first, so when I first met her in 2007 at fifteen, I thought of her as the crazy lady who adopted children with special needs and went around the world fixing other children with special needs. While this was accurate, now she was here to fix my special brother, and I felt wary of this stranger who claimed to know what my little brother needed better than we did. By the time I had my first neurofeedback session, Lynette had already been working with my brother for about a year, yet I was still unsure of her. The only reason I agreed was because my mom told me it would help with my studies. So, one afternoon, Lynette came into my bedroom and sat on the floor with me. At first I felt shy, but her manner quickly put me at ease, and she was so genuine in the way she listened to me that I began to trust her. Before starting, she asked lots of questions about my needs and preferences:

"Do you drink coffee? How do you feel when you drink coffee?"

"Do you drink wine? How do you feel when you drink wine?"

"Do you take a long time to fall asleep?"

"How do you feel when you wake up in the morning?"

"In general, do you get more depressed or angry?"

"How are you socially?"

"How is your focus?"

The list of questions stretched on. I wasn't sure what information she was looking for since her questions weren't like the ones a therapist would typically ask. I noticed that she didn't write anything down; it felt like we were having a friendly conversation. She seemed to relate to my answers and, most importantly, helped me understand my behaviors and how neurofeedback could be beneficial.

At that time, I had a short attention span, I daydreamed a lot, and my mind often felt foggy, which meant I struggled with my studies and my attitude in school. I had difficulty with language processing, communication, and expression. I also found being in large groups tiring and preferred only having a few friends. I would often hide in my room blasting music and found it soothing to tune into the different sounds. But what I struggled with the most were my extreme mood swings. I referred to them as my "on," "off," and "hyper" moments to let my loved ones know how I was feeling so they could adjust their expectations accordingly. When I was "on," I felt able and capable of doing the everyday tasks asked of me. Then, out of nowhere, I would be "off" and lose all focus and interest in my surroundings and was unable to recharge. While I shifted between these "on/off" moments throughout the day, I would sometimes switch to being "hyper." In this phase, I would be in high spirits—singing, dancing, talking loudly, running, or moving around a lot. These shifting states were exhausting and often left me feeling depressed.

None of it made sense until Lynette told me that she'd concluded from my answers that it was probably due to my brain being in a constant low-energy state (akin to ADHD, although she didn't share this with me at the time). It took a lot of effort for me to use this low energy to perform and explained why I so often found things difficult to deal with. It also explained why I would revert to being "off" when my brain ran out of energy from being "on." My "hyper" moments was my brain trying to compensate for that effort of being "on." Hearing Lynette's explanation, I felt like I'd fit a key into a lock—I finally understood. It wasn't my fault; it was my brain, which was both comforting and empowering. On top of all this, Lynette described how neurofeedback could help my brain function better by giving it more energy. I was skeptical but also intrigued.

Lynette attached the sensors to my head and asked me to watch a video game. Thirty minutes later, I was "on," only this time, it was on purpose. I didn't have to wait for my physiology to shift; I could make it happen myself.

After that first session, neurofeedback slowly became an important part of my life, and it was brilliant.

My Journey with Neurofeedback

Initially, I was motivated to continue the sessions because I wanted to pass my French Baccalaureate. In eleventh grade, I was told that if I failed my last semester, I would be kicked out of school—which also explains the pressure I was under. My mom did about thirty neurofeedback sessions on me over the following year (yes, it was my incredible mom who took the lead in doing neurofeedback on my brother and me). The first benefits I experienced were mood and energy changes. I was more aware of my states and better able to control them. I felt sad way less often, and I was more sociable. I had more energy, and I was more focused and better able to concentrate—no foggy mind anymore. Little by little, I began to enjoy reading more and was able to spend more time studying. My thoughts became clearer, I didn't feel so intimidated by longer pieces of text, and my writing during exams improved. Ultimately, I felt more balanced and regulated, which meant I had, or at least felt like I had, more control over my state of mind.

At that time, in 2009, it still wasn't acceptable to talk about mental health issues. It felt wrong to have a brain imbalance or do neurofeedback, as though I was a guinea pig. In retrospect, I realize this was due to a lack of mental health awareness. Many of the other students might also have had a brain imbalance, but it wasn't appropriate to talk about it. Instead, we were labeled as "bad," "misbehaving," "defiant," or "failures." The French high school I attended resorted to toughness, punishment, and breaking students down rather than asking why learning was more challenging for us.

I felt I was one of the lucky ones and was confident in the value of neurofeedback because of two striking moments when I knew the changes could have only been due to neurofeedback.

The first time was when I was playing tennis. My "off" moments always seemed to come in the middle of the game and messed up my play. When I warned my coach, he'd say, "Stay focused." Over the years, he repeatedly told me, "Louloua, look closely at the tennis ball," leaving me frustrated because I thought I was. Then, one day, everything changed. For the first time in the four years that I'd been learning, I was able to watch and focus on the tennis ball coming closer to me and then hit it accurately. It was so exhilarating. I was able to play without breaks and stopped having "off" moments.

The second time was when I was learning to drive. Getting your driver's license in France requires many hours of practice in a manual car, and many people find it hard to pass their test. My driving instructor kept nagging me to focus on the side mirrors. It was hard enough to operate a manual drive and not kill anyone, let alone look at the side mirrors. He constantly battered me about it, and I left my lessons exhausted. And then, one day, my driving experience completely changed; I literally felt my brain multitasking to operate the car and drive safely.

You might argue that those changes were inevitable with practice. While this is true to a certain extent, neurofeedback facilitated and sped up this process. Alternatively, you might think that these changes were entirely due to receiving treatment. However, please note that neurofeedback requires perseverance and willpower to achieve lasting change. In both playing tennis and learning to drive, I was motivated to improve—the neurofeedback sessions helped me feel clear-minded and focused.

Overview of Neurofeedback

At this point, I was so in awe of the changes that I decided to learn more about neurofeedback. I turned to Lynette's book *Miracles Are Made (M.A.M.)* for a better understanding. I was intrigued by the following questions about neurofeedback. These are the same questions I now hear most frequently from my clients. Answers courtesy of *M.A.M.*

Louloua: What is neurofeedback?

M.A.M.: Let's begin with what it's not. Neurofeedback is not an intrusive therapy wherein electricity or radio waves or magnetic influences are entering the brain and forcing a change. Neurofeedback is just an information system teaching to your neurons in the very moment that they fire. It is operant conditioning[7] for the brain, and its magic comes from the speed of the delivery system: the time-lapse between neuronal activity and computer response is only a handful of milliseconds.[8]

Neurofeedback is site-specific brain wave information being fed back very quickly to the brain, causing changes in emotions and behavior to be experienced almost immediately.[9]

Doing neurofeedback is not unlike having a practitioner listen to your heart with a stethoscope and then, having found it running at too fast a pace, put it up for you to observe on an EKG screen. If he then taps a rhythm on your wrist and instructs you to match your heart to this rhythm, your heart will slow accordingly. With neurofeedback, we don't tap a beat on your wrist; instead, we speak to the brain through the use of beeps. We entertain and train the brain by having the person attempt to run a video game simply by shifting his focus and changing his brain wave activity. With the heart example, we listen through a

7   Leslie H. Sherlin et al., "Neurofeedback and basic learning theory: implications for research and practice," *Journal of Neurotherapy* 15, no. 4 (2011): 292–304.

8   Lynette Louise, *Miracles Are Made*, 95.

9   Lynette Louise, *Miracles Are Made*, 20.

stethoscope and display the visible rhythm on an EKG screen; with the brain example, we use sensors on the head and display the activity on an EEG screen. In both cases, the task the patient is being asked to accomplish sounds impossible but is, in fact, simple and easy to do.[10]

Louloua: What does neurofeedback actually do? How does the system work?

M.A.M.: The client has brain wave sensors pasted to his head, and his EEG is sent to a therapist computer. The therapist computer then "talks to" another computer upon whose screen one can observe a computer game in progress. Whenever the brain wave combinations that the client generates moves towards a greater state of balance (determined by the therapist), the game beeps (see figure 1). Since the client is alive (one would hope) and is already generating brain waves, all the therapist does is set the parameters of her computer in such a way that the brain can't help but get a goodly number of "lucky" beeps. Once the brain understands what it needs to do in order to keep the beeps beeping, it tries to go to that combination of brain waves more often. Thus, it changes itself in an attempt to get more. (Understand that brain waves are related to neuronal firing, which is related to neurochemical release.) At this point, the therapist can—like any good coach or personal trainer—up the bar and ask the brain to move even more toward a brain wave representation of neuro-typical firing and/ or ask it to maintain this balanced firing for longer and longer periods of time. The brain starts to do the dance of "chasing" after control; and the changes created, once it learns the steps required for it to lead in the dance, can be quite profound.[11]

---

10   Lynette Louise, *Miracles Are Made*, 10.

11   Lynette Louise, *Miracles Are Made*, 125–126.

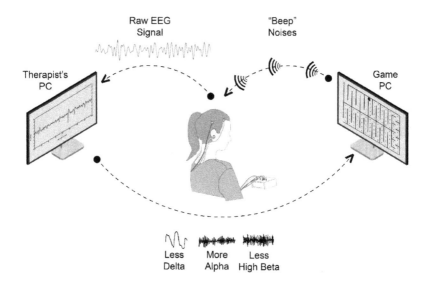

Figure 1: The schematic process of neurofeedback. Sensors are placed on the client's scalp. The EEG is measured and read on the therapist's computer. The therapist sets the parameters for the desired brain wave combination. When the brain waves change and move into balance, the computer beeps, which acts as a reward to the client. The client is seated, playing a video game.

To help you imagine the games, I'll describe a simple one called Mazes. It has a little Pacman head moving through a maze and eating dots. Whenever Pacman eats a dot, the game "beeps" and, as you now know, when it beeps, the connected brain hears "Oh yes, brain. Oh do that. Good, brain, good." Now when Pacman doesn't eat, Pacman doesn't beep, and when he doesn't beep the brain hears "Oh no, no, no, no. Now, brain, listen up, you two neurons, we're saying don't fire." It's kind of like Pacman is spanking the synapse and saying, "Don't fire, don't fire, don't fire so many of those sleepy time waves right now—he's trying to be awake." So, with neurofeedback, your neurons "listen" to me tell them how to fire and your synapses respond.[12] (See figure 2.)

---

12 Lynette Louise, *Miracles Are Made*, 142–143.

Mazes - Fixed Dots

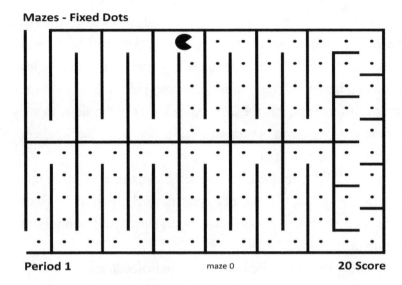

Period 1   maze 0   20 Score

Figure 2: Depiction of a neurofeedback game from the EEGer software while a session is running: The Pacman eats a dot (visual reward) while at the same time the game "beeps" for an audio reward.

So, we teach the brain by rewarding it with beeps in the same way that parents teach the brain with a reward system that uses "yes." The reasons for the success of this therapeutic approach are no more magical than the reasons for the success of your parental one.[13]

Louloua: Why is neurofeedback referred to as "natural"?

M.A.M.: The thing about neurofeedback is it simply mirrors life. That is why we use the term "natural" when referring to it as a therapy. It is feedback, and life is feedback, and this is why so many teaching approaches can have—up to a point—such similar impacts, because every teaching therapy gives feedback. Every sensory integration technique, speech, and occupational therapy gives feedback. Every moving, breathing, happening, other thing in your world gives feedback.[14]

---

13   Lynette Louise, *Miracles Are Made*, 126.

14   Lynette Louise, *Miracles Are Made*, 54–55.

Feedback itself is built into our very reality. Things like temperature, digestive comfort, and fabric texture are all forms of feedback. This cohesive, constant inputting to the brain via every one of our working senses is what binds all the therapies together and makes logical the fact that so many different approaches can help to heal the brains of so many different people. Neurofeedback uses technology to shorten the time span between action and information/feedback, effectively speeding up the rate of change.[15]

Responding to behavior in a noticeable manner, whether it comes from the computer, the sensory system, or the parent IS feedback. Brains use feedback to direct their growth patterns. Responding faster cures quicker.[16]

Louloua: What are the benefits of neurofeedback?

M.A.M.: Changes in your brain lead to changes in how you experience your body, your ability to attend, and your desire to become more than what you already are. Changes in your brain lead to changes in everything. Neurofeedback changes brains. The power of neurofeedback, as opposed to everyday feedback or therapy feedback like acupuncture, which gives messages from the peripheries of our nervous system, comes from its speed of delivery to the neuron and the ability to be site-specific. In other words, with neurofeedback, you give the information to the brain before the peripheries know anything about it. You also give the feedback to the brain before the body turns that brain wave activity into a behavior that is then resistant to change. Even more powerful is the fact that you can give the information to the actual site of greatest neuronal dysregulation by placing the sensor in the spot that is most out of balance and then feeding back to the brain information on how to correct that dysregulation and improve its functioning. Thus it is that neurofeedback has the ability to teach

---

15   Lynette Louise, *Miracles Are Made*, 47.

16   Lynette Louise, *Miracles Are Made*, 13.

us how to tune up and rebuild our own motherboard to a degree and at a level that was previously unheard of. We do this while simultaneously refining our understanding of the software being inputted by the world around us. Therefore, we reeducate ourselves as the drivers of our own lives.[17]

When talking to a particular part of the brain via neurofeedback, I can do more than just tell someone WHY they shouldn't believe in that fear-creating psychological construct they bought into in order to justify the reason for the emotion they are experiencing. It means I can use the "beeping" (think homing signal) instructions of the neurofeedback computer to tell the actual fear-firing amygdala (small almond-shaped nuclei buried in the limbic system of the brain and responsible for most of your flight-or-fight reacting) HOW to not fire those feelings of fear in the first place. In easier-to-understand words, instead of "getting over it," you get to "not have it." Now that's an advantage.[18] (See figure 3.)

THE ADVANTAGES OF NEUROFEEDBACK

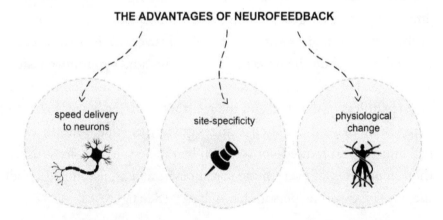

speed delivery to neurons

site-specificity

physiological change

Figure 3: The advantages of neurofeedback, as explained by Dr. Lynette Louise: speed of delivery to the neurons, site-specificity, and physiological change that happens.

---

17   Lynette Louise, *Miracles Are Made*, 53.

18   Lynette Louise, *Miracles Are Made*, 55.

Louloua: Does neurofeedback make all other therapies unnecessary?

M.A.M.: It is impossible for the parent to replace the therapy itself just as it is impossible for the therapy to replace the parent: they are different things. True, the beauty of neurofeedback is its speed of delivering input to the brain. Thus, in a sense it seems to be better at doing what parents and teachers do than they are—precisely because much like the microwave is to cooking, neurofeedback is to brain development—faster—than the old fashioned "do this but don't do that" brain learning way. Still, it doesn't replace the old; it simply adds to it some new advantages. This is because, though neurofeedback teaches the brain how to rebalance itself and learn more easily, it doesn't tell it what to learn. That is your job. Brains need parents and teachers to show them what and who they should become. Brains need a reason to heed the "moral fiber of society's feedback" in order to change themselves in that direction. So, it's up to us—the parents and professionals—to try and make changing in the direction of responsibility, acceptance, and love desirable. However, even with all the right familial support, employing all the right therapies intent on optimizing the rate of positive change, brain health can remain elusive. This is because even if you can speed up the process and even though, if you move faster, you get farther (in fact, processing speed is almost the definition of IQ), regardless of that fact and the fact that neurofeedback is able to help a brain make the desired changes quickly, even neurofeedback is still limited. It is limited not so much by the person's diagnosis as by the combination of everything: social environment, psychology, and the physiology of the person themselves.[19] (See figure 4.)

---

19   Lynette Louise, *Miracles Are Made*, 54.

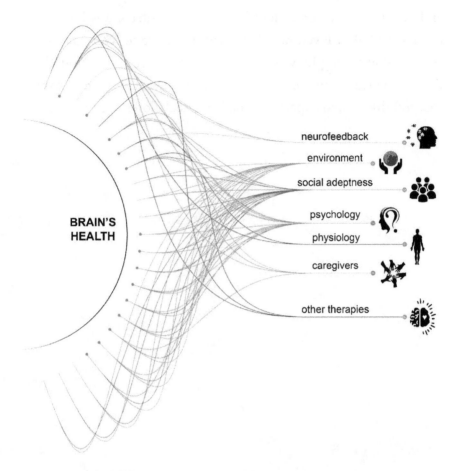

Figure 4: The elements of brain health, as explained by Dr. Lynette Louise. The graph shows how all the elements are interconnected and affect each other. Healing will be dependent on placement of each of these elements.

I remember reading *Miracles Are Made* for the first time. I loved the science behind neurofeedback; it was all so congruent. And I could see the truth in it too. When I felt regulated, it was easier to process what was going on around me, and I could do the things I set my mind to. I saw the same thing with Milo. When Milo had a session, his body would settle and his mind would slow down. He could then process his surroundings better, which spiked his curiosity to explore the places and people around him. I loved how neurofeedback was helping us, but most of all, I loved how it helped me relate to Milo and to the comfortable feeling he was getting from those sessions. Now that I could understand my shifts, I was able to appreciate his potential shifts, too, and this shared experience made me feel closer to him.

TAKEAWAYS

❖ Neurofeedback provides moment-to-moment information on the state of an individual's physiological functioning. It facilitates changes in brain wave patterns and strengthens neuronal pathways as it brings about a functional reorganization in the brain toward balance by using the information from the feedback and increasing mental endurance and flexibility.

❖ The software reads and measures brain wave activity by utilizing sensors placed on the scalp and amplifying the brain wave information on a computer monitor in real time.

❖ The power of neurofeedback comes from 1) its speed of delivery to the neuron, 2) its ability to be site-specific, and 3) its ability to create physiological change. Unlike medication, neurofeedback teaches the brain how to perform better, conditioning it to be in a more regulated state.

❖ Neurofeedback is safe because it is reversible. Through repetition, it becomes permanent.

❖ Parents and teachers teach by using a reward system that uses yes and no. Similarly, neurofeedback uses a video game that provides auditory and visual rewards.

❖ If the brain activity changes toward the desired direction, a beeping sound and visual reward are presented in real time. If the brain wave activity regresses away from the goal, no feedback is given.

❖ Brain health and healing are dependent on the place, interconnectivity, and effect of each of the following elements: psychology, physiology, caregivers, other therapies, neurofeedback, environment, and social adeptness.

CHAPTER 4

The Basics of Neurofeedback

B efore we go any further, I'd like to share my interpretation of the basics of neurofeedback. Below is my summary and interpretation of Lynette's personal teaching to me, John Demos' book *Getting Started with Neurofeedback* (2005), as well as Dr. Ed Hamlin's course entitled "EEG Neurofeedback in the Clinical Practice."[20] These basics also cover the information Lynette teaches her clients so they can continue their neurofeedback therapy after she leaves. There are many types of neurofeedback; what follows only applies to traditional frequency training (we aim to inhibit certain brain wave frequencies while reinforcing others) specifically using the neurofeedback system from EEGer4. Please refer to Marzbani, Marateb, and Mansourian (2016)[21] for a comprehensive review.

Brain Waves

Information comes into the brain from the external world through our senses and is converted into a complex mix of electrical and chemical energy. Electrical pulses are produced as a result of neurons being activated. To record the electrical activity of the brain, also known

---

20   Dr. Hamlin is an expert in the field. This introductory course is taught in conjunction with EEG Education & Research (http://www.eegspectrum.com/upcoming-training/).

21   H. Marzbani, H. R. Marateb, and M. Mansourian, "Neurofeedback: a comprehensive review on system design, methodology and clinical applications," *Basic and Clinical Neuroscience* 7, no. 2 (2016): 143–158.

as brain waves or neural oscillations, we use an electrophysiological monitoring method called electroencephalography (EEG), which uses non-invasive electrodes placed on the scalp. EEG measures the fluctuations of voltage from the neurons' ionic current and records brain waves over some time. An EEG electrode reads the synchronous activity of about 100,000 pyramidal neurons. Brain waves are identified by their frequencies and amplitudes. Frequency indicates the speed at which the wave oscillates, which is measured in Hertz (number of waves per second = Hz). The higher the Hz, the more cycles per second, the faster the brain wave (see figure 5). Amplitude refers to the power of these waves measured in microvolts.

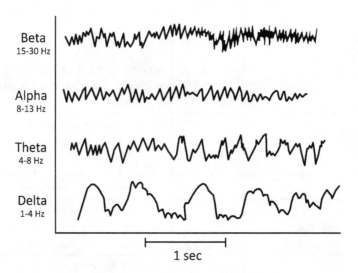

Figure 5: Brain waves' cycles per second

Information travels around the brain in networks, and brain waves are important because the firing of the brain waves correlates with the firing of neurochemistry. Whether there is a dopamine depletion or serotonin excess, changing how the brain fires and what it fires will change how you are and feel. The EEG relates to states of brain functioning, and the patterns of brain wave activity vary depending on their location in the brain, the current activity, and our mental state.

Brain waves frequencies are divided into bandwidths—generally slow, moderate, and fast waves—to describe their functions and provide a representation of the person's state. Each of these frequencies is represented in the brain at all times, while amplitude variations are dependent upon the activity that the person is engaged in, anatomical variation, and the location in the brain. The categories of brain wave frequency bandwidths with their associated names and the states created by a ***preponderance*** of that particular bandwidth grouping are:[22]

Common brain wave frequency bandwidth	Frequency range (Hz)	General states
Delta	1–4	Sleep, repair, complex problem-solving, unawareness, deep-unconsciousness
Theta	4–8	Creativity, insight, deep states, unconsciousness, optimal meditative state, depression, anxiety, distractibility
Alpha	8–13	Alertness and peacefulness, readiness, meditation, deeply-relaxed
Lower alpha	8–10	Recalling
Upper alpha	10–13	Optimize cognitive performance
SMR (sensorimotor rhythm) over the sensorimotor cortex	13–15	Mental alertness, physical relaxation
Beta	12–20	Thinking, focusing, sustained attention, tension, alertness, excitement
High beta	20–32	Intensity, hyperalertness, anxiety
Gamma	32–100	Learning, cognitive processing, problem-solving tasks, mental sharpness

22   H. Marzbani, H. R. Marateb, and M. Mansourian, "Neurofeedback: a comprehensive review on system design, methodology and clinical applications."

Training

Depending on the objective in mind, we want to simultaneously decrease the amplitude of some frequencies and increase the amplitude of other frequencies. The idea is to train down any EEG excesses in a location and train up EEG deficits in a location. As the EEG relates to states of brain functioning, it is generally observed that training to increase the amplitude of higher frequencies translates into feeling brighter, while increasing the amplitude of lower frequencies generates a feeling of increased calmness. For example, low-frequency neurofeedback training can improve the symptoms of autism, as it is usually characterized by too much brain wave synchronicity (too many neurons firing the same thing at the same time), by an overfiring amygdala, and by a confused sensory system with inflammation in the right temporal lobe (that acts as if the patient is being attacked when anything around them moves quickly). On the other hand, high-frequency neurofeedback training can improve the symptoms of ADHD as it is often characterized by an abundance of slow brain waves and a diminished quantity of fast brain waves.

Yet these are general statements and it is all dependent upon the original state of the brain that is being trained. If you are unaware of the original state, you can sometimes train in ways that lead to the opposite effect of what you hoped for. This is similar to expecting a cold medicine to calm a child and finding it actually increases their hyperactivity rather than putting them to sleep. All effects depend upon the *original state* of the person being affected. This is where observation and behavioral assessment come into play.

A neurofeedback protocol includes three elements: the length of time of the session, the location of the sensors, and the frequencies we choose to inhibit and reward. Depending on the state, challenges, and objectives of the patient, we are going to work around different locations and frequencies. For example, a common ADHD protocol would be to reward beta (13–20 Hz) and inhibit theta (4–11 Hz) at Cz (center of somatosensory and motor cortex).[23]

To reduce the predominance of activity of a certain frequency group, we set the game to work better when the activity of this frequency group decreases in amplitude and its opposite increases in amplitude. For example, to decrease the activity of low waves, we set the game to work better when higher frequencies grow in amplitude and lower frequencies decrease in amplitude. We are teaching the brain that "no" means "not so much, especially not now." Decreasing the amplitude of a frequency is accomplished through the use of an inhibit threshold. Increasing the amplitude of a frequency is accomplished through the use of a reward threshold.

In order to make the desired shifts to brain wave activity, the clinician sets thresholds to indicate what activity they want more or less of in order to trigger a reward/beep. In order to decrease the amplitude of a frequency group, we use an inhibit threshold, which means that a beep will occur only when the amplitude average of that group is below the set threshold. (Inhibit thresholds are set above the average amplitude of the frequency group.) In order to increase the amplitude of a frequency group, we use a reward threshold, which means that a beep will occur only when the amplitude average of that group exceeds the set threshold. (Reward thresholds are set below the average amplitude of the frequency group.) However, for a beep to occur, both of these conditions must be met simultaneously.

Brain Areas

When talking to a specific part of the brain via neurofeedback, we use the beeps as instructions to communicate to this particular site, such as the overfiring amygdala that is signaling danger when there isn't any. The beeps signal the amygdala to slow down and not fire so

23   H. Marzbani, H. R. Marateb, and M. Mansourian, "Neurofeedback: a comprehensive review on system design, methodology and clinical applications."

frantically, as this is accompanied by the excessive release of hormones related to chronic stress. Thus, the beeps signal the brain to slow down and not feel these fear feelings in the first place.

We activate the brain area and its associated networks beneath wherever we place the electrodes. Thus it is crucial to have a good understanding of brain anatomy. Below is a simplified summary of the key functions of relevant brain areas (see figure 6).

The brain's cerebral cortex (the outermost layer) is divided into two hemispheres lengthways. The left hemisphere is usually the dominant one; it is detail-oriented and is responsible for verbal expression and understanding, math, logic, and analytical reasoning. The right hemisphere helps see things as complete units, governs our emotions, and is responsible for creativity, perception, visual-spatial processing, and facial recognition.

The cerebral cortex is divided into four different lobes with distinctive functions:

- frontal lobes: memory, attention, character, motivation, social awareness
- parietal lobes: spatial awareness, complex grammar, math, and object naming
- temporal lobes: verbal memories, reading, language, emotions, music, memory, and auditory processing
- occipital lobes: visual processing center

Other relevant structures in the brain with their associated functions include:

- sensorimotor cortex: conscious control of muscle and signaling of where bodily sensations originate
- cerebellum: coordinates voluntary movements, balance, and posture
- amygdala: stores unconscious memories and emotional memories, fight-or-flight response when faced with a perceived threat

– hippocampus: stores conscious memories
– thalamus: relays sensory and motor signals, involved in consciousness, regulates sleep and wakefulness
– hypothalamus: controls body temperature, hunger, thirst, fatigue, and circadian cycles

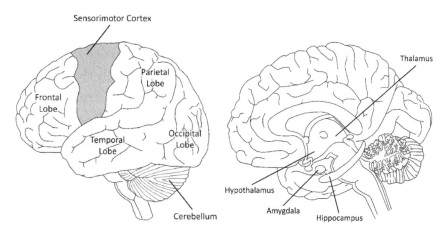

Figure 6: In the two images above, the brain illustrations show the frontal, temporal, parietal, and occipital lobes, the sensorimotor cortex, the cerebellum, the amygdala, the hypothalamus, the thalamus, and the hippocampus.

With neurofeedback, the location of scalp electrodes is determined by an internationally recognized method called the 10/20 system. Each location is defined by a letter to illustrate the brain area and a number to illustrate the hemisphere area. The 10/20 system refers to the distances used between adjacent electrodes of either 10% or 20% of the total distance of the skull between front-back and right-left. Even numbers indicate right-hemisphere training (2, 4, 6, 8); odd numbers indicate left-hemisphere training (1, 3, 5, 7); F refers to Frontal, T refers to Temporal, C refers to Central, P refers to Parietal, O refers to Occipital, and Z refers to the centerline that separates left and right hemisphere (see figure 7). To make this easier to understand, it is best to think of the skull like a globe and the mapping system as lines of longitude and latitude. Neurofeedback training aims to change the amplitude of selected frequency bandwidths under one or several brain locations. Traditionally, therapists use unipolar and bipolar montages. In unipolar montages (e.g., train at T4), we place one active electrode on the skull according to our treatment plan, and we compare that signal to the signal being measured by a second referential electrode, which we usually place on the ear due to its neutral activity. The signal of the active electrode minus the signal of the reference electrode indicates the brain activity under the active electrode. In bipolar montages (e.g., train at T4-P4), we separately place two active electrodes on the skull according to our treatment plan. The obtained signal indicates the difference between the two measured locations.

All of these locations can be found using a tape measure and great precision. However, it is often counterproductive to worry about the exact placement and the cleaning of the scalp. This is a common problem with new therapists. When placing electrodes, it is better to eyeball the placement than to get yourself and your client anxious about the electrodes' exact placement. The whole selected region is doing a similar thing; thus, one or two inches won't matter. Don't be driven by precision, or you will feel stressed worrying about where the sensor should go when you should actually be focused on the client's mood, state, and behavior. If you are working with the brain's feedback loops to send information back to the cerebellum, and your anxiety is making the client anxious, you won't be working on the same brain and, thus, you won't see the right changes.

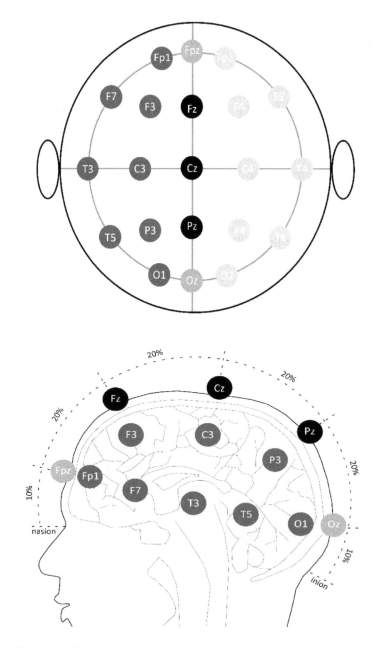

Figure 7: The 10/20 system positions for electrode locations.

Frequently Asked Questions

Here follow the most frequently asked questions about how neurofeedback works. These questions come from me, my parents, and my clients. The answers are from Lynette's book *Miracles Are Made (M.A.M.)*, which has always provided me with the answers I needed.

Louloua: What are the principles behind neurofeedback that make it work?

M.A.M.: Brains are able to organize themselves and learn based on pattern recognition.[24] In this way, they are much like a computer. For example, your computer is capable of everything it's capable of simply because of its ability to recognize coded patterns made from ones and zeros. These ones and zeros are at the beginning of it all. They are called the binary code. It's the same for the brain because the original "machine" language of the brain is a similar kind of yes/no, go/stop, excitatory/inhibitory binary code.[25] You teach with it all the time: Like when your baby reaches to topple the ashtray and is at risk of getting burnt, so you say NO! He stops and then pulls his hand away. At this point, you smile and coddle and praise. He hears, "YES!" This is a perfect example of a parentally executed binary code for the brain.[26]

Children learn and, generally speaking, if we are consistent in our use of "no" and "yes," eventually, our baby learns "not to" and "to." Thus, by giving a consistent response to a behavior, we supply the pattern and teach our children via their brains' remarkable ability to engage in pattern recognition. This is the how of teaching and learning, but it is not the why. You choose to teach, and your child chooses to learn

---

24   Mark P. Mattson, "Superior pattern processing is the essence of the evolved human brain," *Frontiers in Neuroscience* 8, no. 8 (2014): 265.

25   Jeff Hawkins and Ahmad Subutai, "Why neurons have thousands of synapses, a theory of sequence memory in neocortex," *Frontiers in Neural Circuits* 10 (2016): 23.

26   Lynette Louise, *Miracles Are Made*, 121–122.

because the brain has a built-in desire for control.[27] So as long as your child prefers it and sees his life as improved in some way by moving toward an action when you say "yes" and moving away from an action when you say "no," he or she will acquire at least some of the knowledge you seek to impart. Know though that nothing is that simple. For example, some children—especially if their ability to stay focused is compromised because they have something like ADHD—prefer the energy with which their parents say "NO!" to the energy with which they say yes. If your child is like that, switch the energy and give "YES!" a bigger presence or this type of child will learn to do precisely what you wish them not to do. Fortunately, though, for the most part, if all is operating correctly within his/her brain, he/she will just naturally seek the tones and expressions parents tend to pair with the word "yes" to the ones parents pair with the word "no." This preference in the brain is preset, again, by the desire to be in control, because, in general, one feels more in control when receiving approval and agreement than disapproval or disagreement.[28]

In addition, neurofeedback works with the brain's natural inclinations by using preexisting neuronal conditions as tools. In this case, it is the neuron's desire for control that responds to the neurofeedback's beeping sounds and then changes itself, effectively rearranging the maladaptive firing patterns that have been causing maladaptive behaviors: much easier than twenty years on a couch [...] The choosing of whether to move toward or away from (anything) is facilitated by a desire that is shared by all life forms: the desire for balance.[29] You have most likely heard this need referred to as the "Balance of Nature."

---

27   Lauren A. Leotti, Sheena S. Iyengar, and Kevin N. Ochsner, "Born to choose: The origins and value of the need for control," *Trends in Cognitive Sciences* 14, no. 10 (2010): 457–63.

28   Lynette Louise, *Miracles Are Made*, 122.

29   Kelvin J A Davies, "Adaptive homeostasis," *Molecular Aspects of Medicine* 49 (2016): 1–7.

To summarize: It is my supposition that the desire for balance combined with a neuronal need for control and the ability to recognize patterns is the fundamental reason why neurofeedback is such a powerful therapy.[30] (See figure 8.)

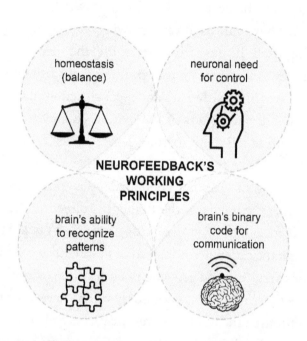

Figure 8: Neurofeedback's working principles, as explained by Dr. Lynette Louise.

Louloua: How do the beeps create change?

M.A.M.: The minute any beeps beep, the neurons—through pattern recognition—begin to notice how these beeps are aligned with their own firing and move toward controlling the sound. As awareness that these moments of alignment mesh with moving toward greater internal balance grows, the brain begins to prefer feeling good to feeling resistant. Thus, since all life is fundamentally predisposed to try to balance itself, once it knows the way, it follows the path to feeling better. In other words, always assuming I've made good therapeutic

---

30   Lynette Louise, *Miracles Are Made*, 125.

choices and am leading the clients toward a more comfortable state when the clients feel better, the neurons will follow the beeps. This happens despite the confusing messages of resistance clients may be giving the neurons via the frontal lobes of their thinking.[31]

Louloua: Are the beeps used to direct growth?

M.A.M.: Your brain is always growing and changing, basically restructuring itself. In the early years of life, the neurons in your left hemisphere are still migrating into position. Your frontal lobes—the part *we think* we think with—are under construction throughout your entire childhood. Since parts of the neuron go and grow where the signals of your life tell them to, the neurofeedback beeps are kind of like a tracking device that beeps faster and faster the closer you get to the right position. Another good analogy is to imagine that your therapist is like the guy with the flashlights directing the plane into position: "Keep coming, over here, keep coming—Whoa! Stop!" It is a good analogy; the difference is instead of flashlights we use beeps—to direct those migrating and growing neurons into position. The beeps truly are like those flashlights because they don't have any more power over the brain than the lights do over the plane. Still, even though he doesn't have to, the pilot follows the beams, just as your neurons follow the beeps. So even though humans are resistant to change because our brains are set up to want control, fortunately, like the pilot who accepts the rules of his vocation, our neurons' vocation is to gain control through pattern recognition and a desire for balance. Neurofeedback uses that reality and benefits from it in order to stimulate change by giving the brain some patterns to look for and try to control.[32]

Thirty minutes or more of beeping brain binary codes can have an amazing impact. So, we use beeeeep to indicate yes or on and an absence of beeeeep to indicate no or off—beeps make the patterns—in

---

31   Lynette Louise, *Miracles Are Made*, 131.

32   Lynette Louise, *Miracles Are Made*, 143.

the auditory form of the binary code. […] Neurofeedback teaches the brain by giving it information—like directions on where to grow. Your brain grows and changes throughout your entire life, so good directions can be invaluable.[33,34]

Louloua: Would it work if the client didn't care about beeps?

M.A.M.: Since most autistic kids appear uninterested in much of what is presented to them, many parents and professionals laugh at the idea that young "Johnny might sit still and allow a stranger to attach wires and sensors to his head so that he can watch a game and listen to beeps." This doubting of the possibility that an autistic child with no interest in computer screens might respond favorably to neurofeedback is why I have spent so much time trying to answer the question of, "What makes the beeps matter?" The answer is "they don't have to matter to the child" because they matter to his brain. Which is fortunate because a lot of what needs to be worked on in the autistic brain are areas unrelated to cognitive thought.[35]

Thus, since all life consistently tries to move toward balance, and since a brain uses pattern recognition in order to accomplish its tasks, that means even non-conscious parts of your brain will try to make the machine beep in an evenly spaced rhythm. And it's your brain's desire to make the machine beep in synchronicity that will lead it to follow the signal in an attempt to balance, even if it has to change itself to do so. And all of this is regardless of your cognizant feelings on the subject.[36]

Louloua: Do you need to stay focused on the game? (Milo rarely focused, so this was of particular interest to me.)

---

33   Stefanie Enriquez-Geppert, René J. Huster, and Christoph S. Herrmann, "EEG-neurofeedback as a tool to modulate cognition and behavior: a review tutorial," *Frontiers in Human Neuroscience* 11 (2017): 51.

34   Lynette Louise, *Miracles Are Made*, 139–140.

35   Lynette Louise, *Miracles Are Made*, 132.

36   Lynette Louise, *Miracles Are Made*, 135.

M.A.M.: Fortunately, the game will work even if the child is zooming around or just daydreaming while I run the machine. And fortunately, the working of the game will affect [sic] change because, contrary to popular opinion, this therapy doesn't care if the child is paying attention with the part of the brain that pays attention because there's so much more to the brain than that.[37]

Understanding neurofeedback means understanding our inner desire for balance, which we more formally call homeostasis (a self-regulating process that maintains the stability of our biological systems by making proper adjustments). Understanding homeostasis means understanding that humans change and grow because they reroute rather than follow a certain model. You'll understand this further in the following chapter of Milo's story.

---

37 Lynette Louise, *Miracles Are Made*, 142.

TAKEAWAYS

❖ The firing of brain waves is in correlation with the firing of neurochemistry; thus, changing how the brain fires, and what it fires, will change how you are and how you feel.

❖ We divide the EEG frequencies into groups of high frequencies and low frequencies with allocated behavioral expectations in various groups of activity. Each of these frequencies is represented in the brain at all times, while amplitude variations are dependent upon the activity that the person is engaged in, anatomical variation, and the location in the brain.

❖ Depending on the objective, we want to simultaneously decrease the amplitude of some frequencies and increase the amplitude of other frequencies.

❖ It is generally observed that increasing the amplitude of higher frequencies translates into feeling brighter, while increasing the amplitude of lower frequencies generates a feeling of increased calmness.

❖ Decreasing the amplitude of a frequency is accomplished through the use of an inhibit threshold. Increasing the amplitude of a frequency is accomplished through the use of a reward threshold. A neurofeedback protocol includes the brain sites, the brain waves, and the duration of the session. Protocols are adjusted accordingly to reach the desired effects.

❖ The principles that make neurofeedback work are 1) our body's reach to homeostasis, 2) the brain's neuronal need for control, 3) the brain's ability to recognize patterns, and 4) the brain's binary code for communication.

❖ How the neurofeedback beeps create change:

- ○ Neurons begin to notice how the beeps align with their own firing and start moving toward controlling the sound.

- ○ Neurons become increasingly aware that this alignment coincides with moving toward a greater internal balance and begin to prefer feeling good to feeling resistant.

- ○ Since all life is predisposed to balance itself (homeostasis), once it knows the way, the brain follows the path to feeling better.

❖ The neurofeedback beeps are used to direct growth because the beeps make the patterns (in the auditory form of the binary code) of information needed to teach the brain. The beeps can be seen as directions for the brain on where to grow.

❖ Neurofeedback works even if the child doesn't care about the beeps because the beeps have to matter to the brain, not to the child. It is the brain's desire for homeostasis that will create change, regardless of the child's cognizant feelings about it.

❖ Neurofeedback works even if the child doesn't pay attention to the game because neurofeedback doesn't need the parts of the brain to pay attention in order to be effective. The brain is more powerful than that.

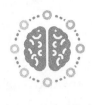

CHAPTER 5

Milo's Unfolding

I closely followed my brother's progress as he trained in neurofeedback through the years. My mom kept a detailed diary of her sessions with him as she was being supervised by Lynette, and I'd like to share it with you. It's important because it shows how he grew, and it gives an account of how to utilize neurofeedback using Lynette's approach. The neurofeedback sessions helped Milo immensely; without them, he probably wouldn't have reached such heights. Through hundreds of neurofeedback sessions, Milo learned and healed. I aim to offer an authentic account of what it's like to undertake neurofeedback therapy, learn from the process, and heal as a result. I've also included the various neurofeedback protocols Milo did at each step. I've included some protocol explanations that I've summarized and interpreted from Lynette as well as the books *Functional Neuroanatomy* by Michael Thompson and Lynda Thompson (2015) and *Getting Started with Neurofeedback* by John Demos (2005).

Realizing Neurofeedback's Potential (2007–2008)

When it was time for Lynette to leave Paris after her first visit, my mom admits it took her some time to feel comfortable with the process of doing neurofeedback. It was my father who had properly understood the scope of the subject and thus had to take the time to explain some important things to my mom before he traveled again. She had to acclimate to using the software and placing the electrodes on Milo's head. Most importantly, she had to learn to trust herself. Lynette made it clear to my mom that Milo's protocols must follow Milo's state and needs. Thus, Lynette always provided detailed explanations to help my mom make more sophisticated decisions regarding the location and frequency changes depending on how Milo was feeling and doing.

For the most part, the sessions were aimed at calming my brother to avoid him throwing tantrums and having meltdowns. Mom also did some brightening to increase his focus and social connection, then calming to help him handle the onslaught of unpredictable behavior by friends and family, and then brightening again with different frequencies in different locations.

After three months of neurofeedback, Milo's tantrums were shorter and less frequent. After a year of neurofeedback, Milo's meltdowns were even shorter (a minute or less), and some days there were none at all.

I could see how hard my parents were working to help Milo, and the results of their labor of love were obvious. Milo seemed more comfortable with his body, he had fewer tantrums, and he learned to deal with them differently. Before neurofeedback, Milo used to wander aimlessly with his helper friends through the streets of Paris in between meltdowns. But as he healed, he enjoyed his walks with family and friends rather than merely relying on them to relieve his stress. His social skills improved, and he became more conversational and less fixated on particular items. For example, Milo used to grab people's watches and purses without asking permission; but as he healed, he was more patient and asked permission.

My admiration for Mom grew stronger as I saw how busy she was helping Milo with neurofeedback. As if our house wasn't crazy enough already, we now had to respect the time and space for Mom and Milo to do neurofeedback sessions almost every two days. Milo's sessions were generally done in the TV room where the computers were set up. While we thought the electrodes lying around were cool, my younger siblings and I were irritated when we had to leave the TV room or turn down the volume so Milo could have his session. My parents always took the time to explain what they were doing for Milo and tried to include us as much as possible. I remember my mom asking me if I saw any changes in Milo after neurofeedback, and she always asked us if we wanted a session ourselves. My parents spent a tremendous amount of time on Milo, but they still gave us our time too.

While Milo's improvements during this first period proved the efficacy of neurofeedback, Lynette pointed out that we would face changes along Milo's healing journey. Although a person with autism will lose some of their symptoms as the condition shifts from a whole-brain disorder to more pinpointed regions of the brain, they can be left with obsessive-compulsive disorder (OCD) or ADHD. She also warned us that people with autism often have an increased risk of a tic disorder or Tourette's syndrome (a syndrome characterized by motor or vocal tics).

And it was true. As Milo healed, he moved away from the typical ASD symptoms and started to show behaviors akin to OCD. For example, Milo would frantically put the house in order, from pillows to clothes to cosmetic products to food to closets to cleaning products … things always needed to be put back at their exact place, facing the right direction, with the caps closed properly. Milo also started to develop a small tic, making grunting noises with his throat.

Summary of Neurofeedback Protocols (2007–2008) (See Appendix III on page 273)

T4, alpha reward (right temporal lobe) to help with:

- calming
- understanding language
- the processing of meaning in speech and vision
- processing sound
- object and facial recognition
- detection and understanding of the emotional tone of voice and states of others
- fear responses
- decision-making

T4–P4, alpha reward (right temporal and parietal lobes) to help with:

- calming
- sensory integration
- social cues and understanding emotions
- working memory, comprehension, and attention
- verbal understanding
- combining auditory and visual information important for reading and writing
- a conscious awareness of visual-spatial events
- understanding temporal relationships
- future planning

F3, low beta reward (left frontal lobe) to help with:

- executive functions
- induction reasoning
- spatial information
- approach behavior and positive emotions
- sustaining attention
- problem-solving
- making judgments and being more sociable
- feeling brighter, happier, and clearer
- improving motivation

Cz, SMR reward (center of somatosensory and motor cortex) to help with:

- sensory integration and getting both sides of body working in concert
- control and organization of voluntary movements
- imagery, verbal encoding, and motor memory
- anticipating and understanding actions
- muscle tone, balance, and fine movement coordination
- attention and mental processing
- reducing hyperactivity
- sleep

Healing Is More Than Just Therapy (2008)

While Milo was still showing improvements, we were reminded that progress isn't linear in the summer of 2008 when Milo was fourteen. Due to a combination of factors—including a urinary tract infection, antibiotics, a gluten-free diet, and potentially wrong neurofeedback protocols—Milo became ill and fell into a small depression. He spent his summer lying on his bed or the floor with his hands behind his head and his legs folded, one over the other. He literally wouldn't move from this position all day and night, and he barely got any sleep. Although he wasn't in an interactive mood, family and helper friends continued to spend time with him—if only to join him in this very still act and try to find ways to get him out of it. While we still engaged in family activities, Milo always reverted back to this position at the end of the day.

Seeing my brother this way was heartbreaking. We were confused and unsure of what to do next. Our family seemed to lack synchrony. My parents did everything they could to pull through. They tried to get Milo's mind and body moving, and always included us. They still had a gift of making everything okay, at least on the outside.

We consulted with Lynette to help us figure out what was going on, but she received mixed messages from us about Milo's situation. When Milo wasn't getting any better, Lynette came back in the fall to help us. To tease out the problem, she decided to sleep over at our house for five days, to ensure that Milo wasn't have seizures during his sleep and to investigate what was going on. I wasn't sure about Lynette staying with us. I had learned to put up a front that everything was all right to other people, so having Lynette stay over meant that there was an issue to resolve. She had the answers, and we didn't.

After the first night, Lynette used neurofeedback and her behavior to brighten Milo and got him out of bed the very next morning. My father pushed Milo to go out for a walk to buy a pack of his favorite chocolates, so Milo and Lynette went out that day, all smiles. They later went out for a bike ride with Tatiana. Within a few days, our Milo was back.

Now that things had calmed down, it was important for the family to understand what had happened. Two main things could have put Milo into this position. First, it seemed that in order to help Milo deal with his symptoms from the urinary tract infection and to offset the tantrums he was having because of the UTI and other environmental factors, Mom had decided only to do calming neurofeedback protocols. Lynette believed that this, in part, had contributed to making Milo low and depressed, and she suggested he might have had too much calming. Lynette explained that just because a particular frequency reward at a particular location works for a while doesn't mean it always will. "You always have to pay attention to the changes in his mood and sleep and adjust the choices for these new states," she explained. Second, Lynette suspected that switching Milo to a gluten-free diet and putting him through an allergy elimination treatment might have overworked him and made him feel miserable and purposeless.

My mother shared with me that this was a critical moment for her. She realized that she had always wanted Milo to be calm, but now that he was, she saw how it made him depressed. The experience changed her perception of healing; her attempt to help Milo not hurt himself actually made his mind shut down so much that he had no purpose or pleasures anymore. We all realized that there is more to healing than just doing all the therapies and using all the tools available. Mom understood that she had been looking at Milo as a set of symptoms and not as a whole. She had overlooked his overall wellness. Now Mom and Dad turned their focus away from the tantrums and began to consider Milo's overall self-regulation. They started to ask what made him feel good.

The image of my brother lying there, looking so skinny and sad, will always serve as a reminder for me of how bad things can get.

Watching him lie there lifeless and stare blankly at the ceiling left me wondering if my brother was having an identity crisis. I didn't recognize him during that period, and I kept wondering what had gone wrong. When Lynette shared her interpretation, I felt sad. I realized we were the ones who needed more learning, not Milo. It was us, his environment, that hadn't caught up with him. While we had made good progress in accepting Milo, we still hadn't truly learned that his happiness came above his autism. While this seems obvious when I see it on paper, realizing it took some time.

Our family knew it was time for a change. While we were already doing the Smadi version of The Son-Rise Program® sessions, Lynette explained how making Milo's program more relevant to his real life would engage him and motivate him. She suggested we start giving him roles and responsibilities. My dad was particularly happy about this approach, as this was always what he aimed for. For example, she told us that letting him choose his own activities and encouraging him to envision where his life was heading would help stimulate his brain. She insisted that Milo needed to feel he was in control of his life.

A lot of readjustments had to be made, on his end and on ours, as Lynette worked her magic to make the whole family feel and work better together. Lynette helped us believe even more in Milo, and thus believe in us as a family.

Summary of Neurofeedback Protocols
(2008) (See Appendix III on page 273)

- **T4, alpha reward** (right temporal lobe)

- **Cz, SMR reward** (center of somatosensory and motor cortex)

Learning to Look at Milo as a Whole (2009)

Lynette started giving Milo new protocols and choices, which my mom could then adapt depending on his specific needs. It was exciting and fruitful. She implemented her Lynette-based play program, which she adapted from biofeedback. When Milo went out for long walks every day to learn about the world, we encouraged him to pay for things in stores and bakeries instead of doing it for him. At first, this was terrifying, but then we learned to hide behind doors and giggle at every mistake or misunderstanding that occurred. In hindsight, I see it was harder for us to watch these mistakes than it was for Milo to experience them. Once again, we realized that we were getting in his way.

This was also a great way to help Milo understand that he needed to earn money in order to buy items that he wanted. Soon he was taking on household chores for Mom in exchange for money or baking cookies to sell to neighbors. Once he had a responsibility to make money and to keep it safe, he bought himself a cute little wallet.

We also made Milo more responsible for the people around him by giving him a defined role with his loved ones. For instance, Milo became Lynette's helper and guide around Paris, since she didn't speak French and he was bilingual. At home, the family counted on him to clean up the plates and set the table (which he loved). We let him choose what he wanted to do during his days, even if it was repetitive—as long as those things meant he could learn and be happy. Slowly but surely, Milo gained beautiful confidence, motivation, and determination.

Milo's days with his helper friends were filled with enjoyable activities. Vera took Milo out for coffee and shopping (and honestly didn't understand how he had autism, which made Milo super at ease with her). Nour created an online blog where Milo could post updates, share food recipes, and write about activities they did together. Aude made documentary movies with Milo about his life in Paris. Tatiana baked, rollerbladed, and went to the pool with Milo. The list goes on and on. Now that I was a bit older, I grew to love each one of Milo's helper friends and was happy when they came over. Mom and Dad set up monthly meetings with the team to discuss Milo's progress and the new objectives—sitting there with them always made me feel so special. Many of them had shared how being with Milo had changed them and their perception of the world. They had made a new friend who didn't care about the world's superficial priorities, and that forced them to do the same. I was so proud to know how Milo touched people's lives and even prouder that he had the loveliest friends to share his life with.

At the same time, Milo's OCD and Tourette's were evolving, as Lynette had predicted. Milo still loved to put the house in order, especially before he left the house, and his grunting tic turned into constant humming sounds. Before long, the whole family (and extended family) knew the music by heart. Lynette explained that it was essential to work together to help Milo find focus and give him the ability to shift into or out of the desired state—for instance, shift out of singing. She explained that he was using the humming and arranging to help himself physiologically. His humming was a way to stimulate himself, the same way keeping the lights on at night helped him sleep. Lynette further explained that, although he was keeping himself busy and doing activities that made him happy, Milo had no job or purpose and had become ritualistic, which increased his OCD.

Lynette thought he was moving into the following three stages at the same time: bipolar (moving from manic to depressive very quickly), Tourette's (OCD, throat clearing), and ADHD (difficulty focusing). My parents told me how it was essential to hear that from Lynette; to acknowledge his progress despite the remaining challenges. They understood that autism is a combination of many brain disorders and that as Milo was healing and meeting new challenges, these disorders

(ADHD, OCD, Tourette's) remained. Lynette asked us to consider this a temporary phase in his healing. It seemed that Milo's teenage years were pulling him apart while neurofeedback kept putting him back together.

We had understood the importance of wanting more for Milo than just stopping the problematic issues he was facing. We realized the power of helping Milo to take care of himself, which would then help with his tantrums and meltdowns. With time, we understood that we wanted him to be able to self-regulate. Neurofeedback helped Milo in so many ways: to feel clearer, express himself, and self-regulate, which ultimately helped him with his tantrums and his processing of the world.

Summary of Neurofeedback Protocols
(2009) (See Appendix III on page 273)

F3–F4, low beta reward (left and right frontal lobe) to help with:

- being less impulsive
- evaluation of incoming stimuli
- planning appropriate response and inhibiting inappropriate response
- reasoning skills
- stretching one's ability to switch between states

C4–F4, low beta reward (right sensory-motor strip and frontal lobe) to help with:

- planning and initiating body movements
- inhibiting responses and behavior control
- empathy, calmness, and emotional processing
- sensory integration
- evaluating the wholeness and context of information and situations

T3–T4, alpha reward (left and right temporal lobes) to help with:

- calming
- comparing present input with past experience, organization of information
- episodic and declarative memory
- grasping the whole picture vs. auditory inputs infractions
- the "what" and "where" of auditory information
- learning disabilities
- the processing of meaning in speech and vision
- word and sentence generation
- decision-making

T4, alpha reward (right temporal lobe)

T4–P4, alpha reward (right temporal and parietal lobes)

What Is Milo's Purpose? (2010)

To support Milo's continued growth, Lynette pushed us to work on his motivation. We had to ensure that he could think long term and had higher self-esteem, which my dad had always strived to give Milo. She insisted on the importance of teaching him independence and life skills. She suggested we start taking the next steps to help him visualize himself in the future. For example, Lynette recommended my parents send Milo to a special needs camp over the summer. While this was unimaginable for my parents at the time, Lynette still wanted Milo to feel it was possible. He needed to see there was a specific path he could follow. Because it wasn't enough to talk about it—Milo needed to visualize it—Lynette had him watch YouTube videos about camps and sleeping away from home. Little by little, Milo believed this might be possible for him. Thinking of Milo sleeping away from home was difficult for my parents at first; my dad was afraid of getting used to living without Milo. But they decided to trust in the process and let him explore. He had his first sleepover in 2010, when he was sixteen, with Tatiana, one of his helper friends and his original shadow teacher, in her family home on the outskirts of Paris. They started with one night away from home, and then a weekend.

For the first time, we started to ask: "What is Milo's purpose?" Lynette insisted that we find him a goal. Could he be a marathon runner? A tour guide? A cleaner? Those questions seemed crazy to us at the time since we had never thought of Milo this way. But our family experienced a notable shift once we started giving him the freedom and independence he needed as a sixteen-year-old boy. We finally grasped what Lynette had meant all these years when she said: "A happy kid is a smart kid." It was true: the happier Milo was, the more capable he was of learning.

Lynette continued to raise the bar and explained that Milo needed to be aware of his health and his autism, of his looks, and of the world around him. She taught us to not be afraid of telling him what we saw so that he could become aware of how others perceive him. For instance, how it frightens people when they see him hitting himself. Lynette pointed out that for Milo to gain social understanding, he had to become aware of his behaviors, his tics, and his stims, such as his humming. So we started to point out the consequences of a tantrum and said things like: "Look, Milo, you're bleeding now and people are scared." Or we would make him aware of his face tapping by saying, "Cute girls won't find you attractive if they see you tapping your face like that." His attraction to girls and women had just started, and we were definitely using it as motivation!

Lynette suggested that we offer him choices when he started to feel tense: "Do you want neurofeedback? Do you want to go for a walk? Maybe having a snack can help you?" Letting him choose made him feel in control. And this is when neurofeedback came in handy: "Do you want to do neurofeedback to ease your face tapping and stop it?" With time, Lynette encouraged us to teach Milo to become a partner with neurofeedback so that he could learn to reach out to it whenever he was in need.

This practice of reaching out to neurofeedback became crucial to Milo. He slowly became aware of how the session could help him. It's important to note how wonderful neurofeedback home training was for Milo because he could do a session whenever he wanted or needed. If my family would have had to go to a clinic for all of Milo's sessions, I believe he wouldn't have been on his way to independence at this point. And even if, hypothetically, Milo hadn't needed neurofeedback as often, it still would have been too inconvenient and complicated for our family.

It also meant the rest of our family could reap the benefits of neurofeedback. As I said earlier, Lynette had helped each one of us with our respective issues. Neurofeedback helped my sister be less sensory sensitive and less anxious about being late all the time.[38] Neurofeed-back helped my little brother be less hyperactive.[39] And, as I described earlier, neurofeedback helped me with my mood, my focus, and my foggy brain. It's interesting to know that doing sessions on the rest of her children actually helped my mom in the process of neurofeed-back. Since we were more expressive than Milo, we were able to share how we felt our changes, which gave her confidence. Finally, I believe sharing neurofeedback at home brought us closer. I would sometimes do a session right after Milo, and I liked to believe that I was not any different than my brother. We were in this together for the long haul.

I think one of the best parts of working with Lynette was that she always explained what Milo could be going through. She provided a story or justification for why Milo was acting in specific ways. Whether it was a physiological explanation or a behavioral one, we understood that it was essential to start with at least a hypothesis to come up with a solution. For instance, she explained that when Milo was hyper and oversensitive, his sensory system had reacted to balance out this feeling, and this was when he needed to scream or tap his face, as a form of relief. Lynette further speculated that Milo's left and right hemispheres were now in hypo-communication (communication below average), which meant it was essential to add new types of protocols. Lynette explained that since we were looking at Milo holistically, we should treat the whole brain rather than only parts of it.

Lynette told us neurofeedback for autism is generally done on the right hemisphere of the brain, seldom on the front or the left, which was problematic since the left and front are equally important, especially at Milo's level of progress. When we worked on Milo in the

---

38   My sister was very picky about the material of her clothes, so she took forever to get dressed and loved to arrive at school thirty minutes early to ensure she wasn't late.

39   He was a wild little boy. Before therapy helped calm him, he would hold little rabbits by their ears, twirl them in the air, and throw them!

left front of the brain, we were working to overwrite beliefs, whereas when we worked on the right front of the brain, we were working to inhibit him from being rude or impulsive.

Summary of Neurofeedback Protocols
(2010) (See Appendix III on page 273)

F4–P4, low beta reward (right frontal and parietal lobes) to help with:

- sustained attention
- abstract thinking and working memory
- understanding intentions
- self-awareness
- governing attention to and interpretation of emotional and contextual cues
- visual-spatial information
- reading, writing, and math

C3, SMR reward (left sensory-motor strip) to help with:

- planning and initiating movements
- motor sequencing, sensory guidance of movement
- rapid, alternating, and smooth sensory-motor movements that are complex and rhythmic, imagining movements
- the processing of emotions related to reflections on self, brightening
- speech, the arrangement of words, language processing, and handwriting
- memory
- problem-solving
- homunculus for right representation in the body (arms, legs, control of the trunk, and proximal body musculature)

C5, SMR reward (left sensory-motor strip) to help with:

- vocal control and mouthing issues
- problem-solving
- planning and initiating movements, motor sequencing, sensory guidance of movement
- attention to visual actions and recognition of objects
- inhibiting responses and behavior control
- affect network
- homunculus for right representation (over the facial sensory area on the right)

C4, SMR reward (right sensory-motor strip) to help with:

- sensory integration, especially if sensory issues present all the time
- monitoring errors and topographic memories
- acoustic rhythms and melodies
- calmness, emotion, empathy
- planning, problem-solving, deductive reasoning
- memory
- planning and initiating movements, motor sequencing, sensory guidance of movement
- rapid, alternating, and smooth sensory-motor movements that are complex and rhythmic, imagining movements

– the processing of emotions related to reflections on self
– calculations
– homunculus for left representation in the body (arms, legs, control of the trunk and proximal body musculature)

C5–C6, SMR reward (left and right sensory-motor strip) to help with:

– calming facial areas that are sensory sensitive
– balancing the two brain hemispheres and feeling more connected to the body
– vocal control and mouthing issues
– drooling

C5–F3, SMR reward (left sensory-motor strip and frontal lobe) to help with:

– vocal control and mouthing issues
– problem-solving, deductive reasoning, and concrete thinking
– planning and initiating movements, language, and speech

P4, alpha reward (right parietal lobe) to help with:

– spatial position, visualization of spatial organization, perception of personal space and spatial relationships
– understanding emotions, nuances, innuendo, and gestures
– drawing and understanding of maps, attention, and working memory

– reducing hypervigilance and anxiety
– sleep
– reading, writing, and solving math
– sustained attention

Pz–Fz, low beta reward (center of frontal and parietal lobes) to help with:

– visual-spatial processing
– attention and comprehension
– pain perception and identification
– the distinction of self from other, reflections on self during decision-making
– the processing of emotions
– calm and slow OCD

F3–F4, low beta reward (left and right frontal lobes)

Cz, SMR reward (center of somatosensory and motor cortex)

T4–P4, alpha reward (right temporal and parietal lobes)

T3–T4, alpha reward (left and right temporal lobes)

T4, alpha reward (right temporal lobe)

Milo's Growth (2011)

The focus for Milo now was to help him structure time, to use his words better, and to acquire life skills such as money management. He was learning to taste what independence felt like through life skills and what happiness felt like through his successes. While we were still working and encouraging him to pay for things on his own, he now had full confidence in his actions and was enjoying his freedom. Milo's favorite pastimes were going to McDonald's, sampling beauty products in Sephora, going to Haagen-Dazs for ice cream, and writing lists on the couch. During this time, we encouraged him to experience the world alone, but there was still work to do in terms of his social skills.

One afternoon, we went to McDonald's together. Milo loved snacking, and he asked me whether he could have a cheeseburger and fries. I explained we'd be eating dinner soon, so he could have either fries or a cheeseburger. He chose a cheeseburger, and we stood in line to order. Suddenly, I realized Milo wasn't next to me and turned around to find him reaching over a stranger's tray to take a big handful of fries. As I ran over to stop him, the man got up from his seat and went to grab my brother (it seemed like he was going for his collar), so I yelled: "Wait, he has autism. He didn't realize what he was doing!" The man quickly sat back down, dropped his eyes to the ground, put in his earphones, and didn't look up again—not even for a second. I asked Milo to apologize to him, but the man seemed too embarrassed to even acknowledge it.

While this incident helped me teach Milo not to take other people's food, it also made me aware that Milo needed to be convinced of social taboos; it would never be enough for him to be told not to do something. We tended not to share our reasons with Milo, but now I understood that properly explaining things to him was crucial to his growth. While it was shocking and scary to watch the man react that way, and while what Milo did was wrong, I walked back home with a smile on my face thinking how Milo appeared to be just a "weirdo" now rather than an autistic person. I was also fearful that Milo would throw a tantrum since he hadn't gotten what he wanted, or because he felt bad for his actions. But he didn't. He apologized to me the whole way home. I was proud of him for how well he reacted.

During this time, there was a particular week when Lynette visited, and Milo was showing enormous development. Slowly his personality was emerging, and he was turning into a strong, adamant, and funny seventeen-year-old young man. One morning, Lynette encouraged my mom to let Milo go outside on his own to the bakery and buy three different pastries for the three of them. This was a big deal for Mom—it was the first time Milo was doing something like this on his own. The bakery was right in front of our apartment, so Lynette and Mom were able to watch him from the window. They witnessed him walking home from the bakery with the three pastries in a bag, but rather than bringing them home, he ate them all. When he got home, he told Lynette and my mom that he threw them in the garbage. Knowing what had really happened, Lynette played along and went to check the garbage with him, which is when he admitted that he'd eaten them. Milo apologized and was really worried that Lynette would be disappointed. Why is this relevant? Because so many people believe that those with autism can't lie. They can!

During her visit, Lynette added a new protocol called "Beta Reset," which consisted of a two-channel parietal field training that would enable Milo's cerebellum to work with his sensory-motor strip to help his balance and body stillness, to help calm his body, and to enhance his communication, depending on how he was feeling. This protocol produced more happiness and better eye contact in Milo. He was calm but socially available, and he was smarter.

The perfect story to illustrate the effect of that protocol happened when we went to my aunt's for Thanksgiving dinner. That night, Lynette came with us, and there was a karaoke machine to entertain the sixty other guests. Milo was now interacting with the people around us, saying hello, and asking them where they had traveled from. Milo seemed so comfortable and, after seeing my best friend and me singing, he asked if he could sing. I asked to join him, but he refused to have me by his side. He picked the song himself, "Yellow Submarine" by the Beatles, and stood to sing all on his own in front of all the guests. I had never seen him at such ease and peace. It was unbelievable. My grandmother and I were so moved that we had to leave the room to catch our breath. It was a beautiful and touching moment.

This wasn't Milo's first time doing karaoke, as this had become a fun activity to do with the family when Lynette was in town. However, this was the first time Milo wanted to sing something on his own. It was moments like these when I wished Milo could express himself more because I was curious to know if he had done this for himself or because his act of bravery would make his family proud.

We were endeavoring to teach Milo good manners, to teach him about friendships and freedom, and to help him find a leadership role in this world. As a result, 2011 was a turning point for Milo, and he actually needed fewer neurofeedback sessions than usual.

Summary of Neurofeedback Protocols
(2011) (See Appendix III on page 273)

P3–P4, alpha reward (left and right parietal lobes) to help with:

- sensory integration
- focus and cognitive reasoning
- auditory processing
- reading and writing
- math and algebra
- geometry and spatial relationships

F7–F8, low beta reward (left and right frontal lobes) to help with:

- repetitive talk and fixations
- spatial, visual, and auditory working memory
- sustained and selective attention
- mood and social awareness

P6–F8, beta reward (right parietal and frontal lobes) to help with:

- spatial and visual working memory
- facial recognition
- mood regulation, calming
- speech and writing
- self-awareness
- sustained attention

P5–F7, low beta reward (left parietal and frontal lobes) to help with:

- verbal expression and fluency
- visual and auditory working memory
- selective attention
- the meaning of words and verbal construction

- face-name associations and sign language
- monitoring color and shape, drawing
- attention to semantic relations and associating words with visual percepts
- reading and orthographic-phonology links

Beta Reset, beta band increment reward every 90 seconds (parietal-occipital) to help with:

- balance
- body stillness
- calmness in the body
- spatial relationships
- social ability
- Parkinson's and Tourette's

P3, alpha reward (left parietal lobe) to help with:

- cognitive reasoning and problem-solving
- attention
- imagination and association
- spelling, handwriting, and complex grammar
- math and recall of series of numbers
- verbal comprehension
- dyslexia and algebra
- hypersensitivity or sensory defensiveness

Pz–Fz, low beta reward (center of frontal and parietal lobes)

Becoming Independent (2011–2014)

When my parents saw how much Milo enjoyed his first sleepover, they decided to send him to a special needs summer camp, as Lynette had previously suggested. We usually spent half the summer in Lebanon, and there was a school for special needs there called Step Together that hosted a residential camp. After my parents and Milo's first visit, they were immediately convinced.

Step Together provides education for children and adults with intellectual and developmental disabilities through a holistic approach in providing therapy and teaching independent living skills. The association follows philosopher Rudolf Steiner's principles by seeking a deeper understanding of the human being as a whole while developing social, ecological, economic, medical, spiritual, and educational aspects. The Step Together community is a place of hope, where everyone learns to love and to give. Step Together's distinct identity is evident in its natural environment in the middle of the Lebanese mountains, its eco-friendly buildings, and the different colors and elements of its classrooms.

Milo first spent a couple of nights there in the summer of 2011, which then extended to a week. My parents were impressed with how well Milo handled it, and also with how well they were able to handle it. Little did they know this would be the first step to helping Milo's independence blossom.

After hearing about Milo's time at the camp, Lynette joked one day that he and Mom should visit her in Los Angeles. Traveling to the other side of the world wasn't something my mom was interested in doing, but the idea of the trip caught Milo's attention. Over the years, Milo had grown fond of traveling: where he had traveled in the past, where he would travel in the future, and especially where his loved ones were going. Traveling for Milo had become his way of placing himself and his loved ones in time and in space, especially since our extended family is scattered all over the world. And travel became a subject of conversation he could have with anyone he met. Thus, the concept of traveling to Los Angeles to stay at Lynette's house grew fiercely and passionately in his mind. I'll never forget the time we were having lunch with my family and Milo looked up from his plate and asked with full seriousness when he was going to visit Lynette, and he made sure we understood he was going on his own. We were astonished, but it was clear that he had decided. Just like that, Lynette picked Milo up in Paris (she was on her way back home from another work trip in Europe) and off they went to California in the summer of 2012 when he was eighteen.

Milo's week with Lynette brought him more comfort, ease, and confidence than we could have ever imagined. Milo had a taste of freedom and independence, and he came home wanting more.

When Milo was ready for his next step, my parents went looking for potential colleges abroad for him. Every step we'd taken up to this point had been crucial in encouraging Milo, and all of us, to imagine a time when he could leave home. It was terrifying, but we all had our eyes on the same goal: for him to be happy and self-sufficient.

After researching and making a visit to the Ruskin Mill Glasshouse College in Birmingham, UK, as recommended by Step Together school principal Dr. Reem Mouawad, my parents were convinced it was the right fit. They applied for a place for Milo. An individualized program had to be developed for his admittance, and in January 2013 at age nineteen, Milo left home. My parents went with him, and my siblings and I were left alone in the house. For the first time ever, we were without our Milo. Overnight, our home went from being a crazy house to a dull, silent house. At that moment, all I wanted was to hear Milo's humming. I sat on his bed and prayed he would be happy. Then a thought hit me: *Milo left home before I did … who would have thought?* I smiled.

The Ruskin Mill Glasshouse College is housed in a former glass factory and offers educational and residential provision to young people with a wide range of complex learning, emotional, and behavioral difficulties. Students are placed in team house settings with peers or local families to teach them life skills and increase their independence. It provides an array of craft workshops and artisanship, such as glassmaking, weaving, felting, music, performing arts, and a farm and gardens for mountain biking, animal husbandry, harvesting, and woodland management. It also offers a range of internal and external working opportunities so that the students can develop social and vocational skills.

Every day Milo had access to all of these opportunities, and we could feel the change in him each time he came back to visit us. Milo now had patience, curiosity, and a willingness to learn that propelled him to engage in activities that made him stronger and smarter by the day. When he came home, Mom would do some neurofeedback sessions on him, adapting to his needs. The neurofeedback now acted like a little booster of brain balancing to help him handle college again. There were times when Milo asked for a session, and times when he declined one. We could see that when Milo asked for a session, it wasn't out of routine but out of need.

Milo was making significant progress, and we started discussing the use of social media while he was away and the importance of friendships. In the spring of 2014, we went on a family trip to Austria, just the six of us. Milo's progress was made even more evident during that trip. For the first time, we were able to peacefully enjoy each other's company. We were able to have good conversations with him, and he was hilarious. No more fear of tantrums, no more fear of the unknown, just full faith in him. He was my brother, through and through.

Summary of Neurofeedback Protocols (2011–2014) (See Appendix III on page 273)

- **T4, alpha reward** (right temporal lobe)
- **F3, low beta reward** (left frontal lobe)
- **P6–F8, beta reward** (right parietal and temporal lobes)
- **P4, alpha reward** (right parietal lobe)
- **T4–P4, alpha reward** (right temporal and parietal lobes)
- **Beta Reset, beta band increment reward every 90 seconds** (parietal-occipital)

TAKEAWAYS

❖ Realizing neurofeedback's potential is instantaneous, but it takes time and patience to understand how much it can actually change someone's life.

❖ Healing is more than the therapies a patient receives—it also requires downtime to grow, fun to learn, and love to feel empowered.

❖ Neurofeedback protocols vary according to the needs and growth of the client.

❖ My family learned to look at Milo as a whole rather than looking at his symptoms or skills alone.

❖ "What is your purpose?" is an important question that should drive every parent or child, no matter what their special need or disability.

❖ Independence and freedom are generally the most motivating objectives for children and young adults and should be used as motivation to create change in their lives.

CHAPTER 6

Lessons in Healing

Milo's progress and his healing journey have always been a hot topic of discussion in our family. And as you can see from Milo's story, it is unclear what did what for him. What is clear, though, is how entangled everything was. One thing, a failure or a success, always leads to another, and it is in that flow that we need to trust. Milo's environment had to change for Milo to change, and neurofeedback was there to support all of that and to push him to the next level.

If this had or hadn't happened, would we be where we are today? This is a question I always find myself asking. However, I believe in the saying "It's the journey, not the destination that matters," and this is especially true for people with special needs. Each step of that journey will affect them and their arrival more than the average person.

I was aware of all this, but I needed to turn to Lynette for some clarification about Milo's progress and how neurofeedback had really helped him. During one of Lynette's visits to Paris, we sat on the couch with our coffees, and I presented her with one question after another. Her answers were helpful and enlightening, as always, and I'd like to share them with you now:

Louloua: When looking at the big picture of someone's storyline, how do you credit the progress to neurofeedback?

Lynette: I don't credit all the progress to neurofeedback. When neurofeedback is being used, it causes change. And if you are keeping an eye on the direction of that change, if you are reinforcing what helps, then neurofeedback produces progress.

But I know what you mean. Change can be evident, but where to place the credit is very confusing, especially when helping someone with autism because so many therapies and human elements come into play. With neurofeedback, we're talking to the brain via technology; we are always changing the story. So, if they get better or they get worse, we get the credit, at least in part. We're changing how a person is supposed to act; we're avoiding the creation of memories that reinforce problems and replacing those experiences with new emotions and behaviors. We're asking the brain to learn how to behave differently. Now all these subtle changes make a difference over time, which you can often only see when looking back at everything because, at the moment, they are nothing more than small shifts. However, not everything is subtle. After a neurofeedback session, you can immediately see change, at least in emotion. So, you know you are having an effect. Once you start using neurofeedback, it is impossible to know what would have happened without it because we're changing the story. In Milo's case, it's even harder to give credibility to neurofeedback because of the different treatments that were set up.

On the other hand, you could say that because there were so many different treatments, neurofeedback had to be the primary influence in his improvements. Regardless of credit from a clinician's point of view, you just need to be sure of your intention to improve and help people become who they most want to be. Also, know that if a client isn't being helped to feel better, they won't cooperate, so since your brother asks for neurofeedback, you know it is helping. The good news is that the more he improves, the easier it is for him to improve. Once he knew he could improve, he became more relaxed and continued to improve.

Louloua: Overall, Milo did over five hundred sessions at home. Why did he need so many sessions and so many varied protocols?

Lynette: When a brain is functioning with a whole-brain

dysregulation, when the environment is reinforcing the issues when everything is firing incorrectly in this way, you need that many sessions. It's important to realize how complex a person and his environment can be. Milo had lots of complications and elements come into play during his growth, including a UTI, antibiotics, puberty, family confusion … Your brother had to change and heal inside all of that, between the different pressures from the parents, siblings, volunteers, and teachers. Every time we make a change for the brain, we still have to bring everyone else along. Because when they expect a behavior, they invite that behavior by their action. When they think, *Oh, is he going to have a tantrum?* he will. If we wanted to only fix the tantrums with Milo and didn't have the other elements to correct, if he were a typical man with too much anxiety, then we would have been able to complete his treatment in very few sessions. That's the problem with research studies; they exclude and isolate major factors and try to look at the progress of a singular event, which is not realistic. With Milo, though, we kept raising the bar for him to reach higher objectives each time.

I like to think of the autistic brain like Jenga, the game. It's like a big building that exploded, fell, and is now just a pile that you have to carefully piece out and build back up. You have to fix something new every time you move a piece. You get a new shape, and a new problem arises. It's not surgery with a big bulldozer; it's a subtle step-by-step change, a balancing act. You have to work in the spirit that everything we move, we move to create a stronger brain. This is why we do so many different protocols with autism. And this is also why a home system is so needed. There is no way Milo would have been able to do that many sessions if the system was at a clinic, and he probably wouldn't have been able to be that flexible in his expectations. The main goal at the end of the day is to get his brain ready and to get people ready to receive him.

Louloua: Milo's change wasn't linear. Is this the case for everyone?

Lynette: No human being grows or improves linearly, and trying to make them do so leads to training instead of educating. Generally, training is cruel and limited. It reinforces and/or defeats the animal in us. For example, controlling tantrums by giving treats when they stop leads some children to tantrum for the treat. Punishing for the tantrum leads some children to fight more while other children become placid and unmotivated. The talented teacher or parent understands this and works with more of a gestalt method for change. As you saw, nothing only helps the tantrums. Everything has secondary effects. With neurofeedback, we can make sure those secondary effects are a positive change.

You need a cocktail of medicine to find the right mix, like any doctor. Here, we are teaching the brain how to do this for itself, and through this, there are windows of ease, and it gets tough again. We are creating healing in the brain and teaching in the brain. Each time we go through a problem, we learn something new, and as you saw, Milo got stronger and more available. Humans are gently moving, we go backward and forward. So no, there is no linear change, with neurofeedback or anything else in life. With anything in life, we change, and then we fight the change. There are always good and bad days. The media loves to show the miracle stories, the easy part of things. Even research does this. But this is not the reality of the world. Positive outcomes will always happen, but it is never done linearly. People choose to show either just the good or all of it.

Louloua: My parents never agreed to medicate Milo. However, they were quick to try neurofeedback. What's the difference between teaching the brain with neurofeedback versus medicating it with prescription drugs?

Lynette: What makes neurofeedback so effective is that we are teaching the brain to change itself. Medicating the brain to get to a specific state actually stops the brain from learning how to do that for itself. Medicating leads to dependency and chronic issues while teaching changes in the direction of freedom and wellness and healing.

Also, it is a lot harder to direct medicine and keep it isolated to the correct part of the brain. A good example to explain this is the case of a sixteen-year-old boy with Asperger's that I work with. He was given medicine to stimulate his frontal lobes and improve his focus. Unfortunately, though his frontal lobe function improved, his parietal lobes got worse. They became overstimulated, and this led to his being tunnel focused but aggressive. He tried another medicine to calm that down, but it made him dizzy and nauseous. With neurofeedback, I simply moved the sensor, which effectively isolated the regions I wanted more stimulated from the regions I wanted to remain calm. This taught his brain how to balance the two areas on its own. Within six sessions of neurofeedback, his repetitive conversations and aggression were cut in half.

Louloua: Considering my brother's evolution, how long do you think the effects of neurofeedback will last?

Lynette: A positive aspect of neurofeedback is that its effects continue beyond treatment for the simple reason that once the brain gets a hint of what clarity feels like, the person wants more of it, and thus instructs the brain to continue to function in this way. Additionally, the person now behaves differently. Once people behave differently, the world starts responding differently, too, and thus, the feedback response is different. Hence, they live in a new world that teaches new things. For example, instead of being negatively reinforced by hearing how bad and hyperactive they are, they hear, "Wow, you finished your work quickly today!" or "You were really good at sitting this afternoon." This information helps the brain embrace its own changes and heal itself, as the world the person lives in continually redesigns its feedback by responding to and reinforcing this evolving brain.

Louloua: We did so many sessions. Were we putting the brain in danger in any way?

Lynette: Well, anything that can help can also hurt. However, according to literature, a healthy brain is determined by its ability to switch focus and change states easily but not in a hectic way.[40,41] Thus—as long as the therapist follows the client goals as well as the behavioral responses created by each session—asking the brain to shift systematically is healthy. This understanding means to me that neurofeedback is a fairly safe therapy to apply, again, as long as the person applying the therapy shifts with the client's responses. In this way, even the search to adequately understand each person's brain and to find their correct protocol while changing locations and frequencies is part of the healing process. The agile back and forth between sessions from one state to another exercises the brain and makes it more flexible. In this way, even a therapist's mistakes can become a blessing as long as they are not often repeated. Changing and tweaking protocols in search of homeostasis is part of the journey, nothing is static, and a protocol that was unpleasant before certain brain changes can become desirable after them. In other words, it is safe if you are working together and paying attention. If your therapist doesn't do that and you don't like how you feel, stop going. Your brain will seek its familiar state of balance and find its way back to how it was before neurofeedback, as long as the therapist's mistakes aren't repeated. All brains seek balance based on what they understand as balance.

Louloua: Milo has done years of neurofeedback, and while he has made significant improvements, he still has obsessions and fixations. How do you explain that?

Lynette: With Milo, or any child, you have to think of where he started. Milo used to hit himself, and he was constantly bleeding (although he tried not to hurt himself). His face felt so uncomfortable that he had to grab hold of whoever was around him and slam his mouth and teeth into their shoulders. Now Milo is not violent at all

---

40   Douglas D. Garrett, et al., "The importance of being variable," *Journal of Neuroscience* 31, no. 12 (2011): 4496–4503.

41   Richard F. Betzel, et al., "A positive mood, a flexible brain," *Brain* 139 (2016), 2104–2112.

and has traveled a long distance. His fixations today are much better than they used to be. He now has more control over himself and knows when it is a good time to attend to his fixations. He will continue to grow, and at least now, he has a future. Besides, to be fair, probably everyone else you know has a fixation or two.

Louloua: How do Milo's stims contribute to his self-regulation, and are they supposed to go away during a neurofeedback session?

Lynette: Well, a stim is a response to a need, like all self-regulation. For example, a feeling of restless leg syndrome is common in children on the autism spectrum, so they hit their legs or walk constantly. Lips can tingle or go numb, making speech hard and causing the child to fiddle with their lips a lot. Depth perception can make things look big and then small like an *Alice in Wonderland* world. So, the child may have to touch things constantly to ascertain where they are in space. Once a behavior begins and is repeated because it gives relief, for example, it becomes a habit. A stim (or ism) is an addictive habit. Some stims are misunderstood tics.

Sometimes, the stims will calm down after a session, which would be a sign that the session helped him. But stims are usually the last thing to go if they ever do. Stims aren't supposed to stop during the session, and sometimes they get worse. There have been many sessions with Milo where ten minutes into the session, he intensely/painfully tantrums, or hums loudly … but then he's back to normal, and after the session, he is better than normal. Sometimes as the brain shifts, stims increase. If it's transitional, it's a good thing. If not, change the protocol. I watch the intensity of the stimming behavior, along with everything else, for an indication of comfort … I just don't get distracted by them.

Thanks to Lynette's explanations, Milo's learning curve started to make more sense. My brother's story is as beautiful as it is complex, as are all stories of healing.

I gathered my thoughts and realized that my brother's story illustrates the following:

❖ **Progress is never linear.** Changes often happen simultaneously, and new problems arise as others are being fixed. As Lynette likes to explain, healing usually takes the form of a progressive line graph, with many ups and downs along the way.

❖ **Problems and objectives change as someone heals.** We always need to adapt accordingly. It's important to follow the patient's cues and behavior.

❖ **Look at the person as a whole.** Looking at Milo as a whole rather than his symptoms and skills alone enabled him to flourish. This mentality not only helped him learn more, but it helped us focus on the important things about him.

❖ **Prioritize happiness.** My parents tried many other therapies but, with time, they understood that Milo's happiness and comfort were more important than any other development.

❖ **Environment matters.** You can do all the therapies in the world, but if the environment doesn't change while the person is changing, then the progress will be limited. Family, friends, and teams should follow the individual's rate of progress and not get in the way. On the contrary, the surroundings need to create new opportunities for learning and growth.

❖ **Neurofeedback and life experiences go hand in hand.** Neurofeedback acted as a learning tool for Milo to self-regulate and grow, while new and different life experiences were set up for Milo to learn and flourish. Neurofeedback and feedback from life are inseparable.

❖ **Raise the bar and don't set limits.** We could have been doing all of the above perfectly, but if we hadn't chosen to believe in Milo and in the world, if we hadn't chosen to be brave and get out of our comfort zone, then Milo wouldn't have the life that he has today. More often than not, we are the ones setting limits on ourselves and our loved ones, and as soon as we start letting go and wanting more, then new doors open.

❖ **You can't fix others, you can only fix yourself.** Looking at Milo as a whole and prioritizing his happiness were our ways of not actively trying to "fix" Milo. Importantly, they were our ways of fixing ourselves in terms of our beliefs and actions. Working on ourselves along the way enabled Milo to be free and flourish.

Looking back at my brother's story this way filled me with gratitude. Home training not only offered Milo easy access to a session but also offered a role for my mother in Milo's healing and benefited the entire family. Neurofeedback enabled Milo's brain to change and speed up the healing process, but it was Lynette's style of neurofeedback that made all the difference. Lynette made it clear to us that we had to create new opportunities for Milo to learn. Her play approach enabled us to teach life skills to Milo in a fun, loving, effective way. Her genuine love and belief in Milo and her consistent enthusiasm to keep raising the bar made Milo's healing an enjoyable and considerate process for all.

Following My Instincts

Being part of my brother's crazy ride, I became ever more curious about the possibility of creating the same changes I had witnessed in my brother in someone else. By the time I was in my third year of university in Paris, double-majoring in global communications and entrepreneurship, I had gained a lot of professional experience working in various business fields. However, my interest in special needs and mental health was always in the back of my mind. Especially neurofeedback because I was impressed by the change it had created in my family.

I always found ways to volunteer with special needs people from a young age. I learned and applied behavioral therapies for children with autism, including ABA, in different clinics in Paris, and elements of The Son-Rise Program® at home. I also shadowed some young children at Step Together—the summer camp my brother attended. That experience gave me exposure to working with individuals with special needs and provided knowledge and insights into a positive educational and therapeutic system. The school has over eighty students of all ages on the same campus, and during their breaks the courtyard is filled with students from diverse backgrounds, each one of them thriving, together or on their own.

Those experiences with other behavioral therapies and other children enabled me to contrast Milo's path to others. The most striking difference I noticed was our use of Lynette's play therapy and parts of The Son-Rise Program® at home compared to the use of ABA, the most common therapy for autism. While many have found ABA successful at developing skills and enabling independence, others criticize it for not generalizing lessons outside the therapy room, taking away the child's power and confidence and thus segregating him/her. From my experience and observation, I agree with this critique.

During my yearlong study abroad at Northwestern University in Chicago in the United States, I decided to explore my interests in the clinical and research world of autism and mental health through the university. The more I learned, the more I realized the innovation and importance of neurofeedback therapy.

Upon graduating from university in Paris at twenty-one, I stepped out of my comfort zone and started pursuing a career as a neurofeedback clinician. I began reading all the foundational books about neurofeedback that I could get my hands on. My objective was to try to understand as much as I could about the actual mechanism of how neurofeedback worked.

TAKEAWAYS

❖ Once you start using neurofeedback, it is impossible to know what would have happened without it because you're changing the story; you are creating change in the direction of freedom, wellness, and healing.

❖ The more someone improves, the easier it is for him/her to improve. And once someone knows he/she can improve, he/she becomes more relaxed and continues to improve.

❖ Lessons in healing:

  ○ Progress is never linear; ups and downs are to be expected and problems and objectives change as someone heals.

  ○ We should learn to look at the person as a whole, not just his/her symptoms, and always prioritize happiness over skills.

  ○ The environment needs to change as a person heals to follow their rate of progress. Neurofeedback and life experiences go hand in hand for learning and growth.

  ○ We should constantly raise the bar; we should never set limits on ourselves and our loved ones. Let's aim to be brave and say yes to new opportunities.

❖ Home training offers the advantages of easy access to a session and caregiver empowerment.

❖ Neurofeedback, play therapy, acceptance, and raising the bar are what made my brother's healing considerable and enjoyable.

PART II

THE LEARNING CURVE

Behaviors and disorders can be understood through physiology, which empowers us to think in terms of symptoms rather than diagnosis. Don't let a label speak for itself and stop you from digging. Instead, follow clues in a person's emotional, behavioral, and cognitive responses, and allow neuroanatomy to guide your understanding and your decisions.

Part II is the story of my learning curve while training in neurofeedback under many different experts in the field. We will discover different neurofeedback approaches to healing, and we will learn about the arousal and compensatory lens as an investigative method to discover the cause of a behavior. We will further delve into why it was Lynette's approach that resonated with me the most and explain what makes her understanding so effective and unique. Through my exposure to the field, we will also explore the discrepancies found between the research and clinical worlds and show how that reinforced my belief in using neurofeedback more holistically.

CHAPTER 7

Understanding Behavior through the Arousal and Compensatory Lens

To delve into this world, Lynette recommended I take an introductory course called "EEG Neurofeedback in the Clinical Practice." The course was taught by Dr. Ed Hamlin, who plays a key role in the neurofeedback clinical field, at the Institute for Applied Neuroscience in Asheville, North Carolina. My lack of academic background meant I needed to learn about everything related to neurofeedback—psychology, clinical neuroanatomy, and psychophysiology. But I felt confident I would be able to assimilate Dr. Hamlin's teachings. I wanted to know if neurofeedback could become my future profession, so I went to the class in the hope of finding a clinician looking to hire a neurofeedback technician.

Come fall 2014, as I looked around me at the start of the course, I noticed I was the youngest student in a class of older clinicians and the only one without a relevant professional or academic background. However, I was the only one who had been on the receiving end of neurofeedback therapy, which boosted my confidence.

By the end of the first day, I realized no one was hiring, which meant I had no plan after the course. While the teachings intensified by the day, I started to think about perhaps getting into the device engineering side of neurofeedback rather than becoming a clinician. What was I thinking, wanting to become a clinician? After all, I was already fascinated with the program code and the new emerging trend of brain-computer interfaces. Either way, the course was exactly what I needed; I recommend it to anyone wanting to get into the field.

We were introduced to a model that would forever shape and change my understanding of human behavior, states, and healing: the arousal model.

The Arousal Model

Below is a summary of my understanding of the arousal model, as explained by Dr. Hamlin, along with a further explanation of arousal by Donald Pfaff from his book *Brain Arousal and Information Theory*.[42] I still remember how I felt learning about the arousal model—it was as if all the pieces of the puzzle were finally falling into place.

As Dr. Pfaff explains it, it is our brainstem's primitive neuronal system that activates our brains and behaviors in our central nervous system. The brainstem, the center of the mammalian brain, is in charge of communication between the brain and the body and controls our unconscious functions (i.e., swallowing, breathing, waking up, sleeping, heart rate, consciousness, and blood pressure). All of these mechanisms are referred to as arousal mechanisms, which "determine our responses to the environment, our emotional expressions, and our mental health."[43] He explains that arousal physically manifests in three ways:

1. behavior

2. activation of the electrical activity in the cerebral cortex

3. activation of pathways in the autonomic nervous system

According to Dr. Pfaff, to make shifts to our arousal levels accordingly as we go through our day, five neurochemical systems work

---

42   Donald W. Pfaff, *Brain Arousal and Information Theory: Neural and Genetic Mechanisms* (Cambridge: Harvard University Press, 2006).

43   Donald Pfaff, *Brain Arousal and Information Theory.*

together and use histamine, acetylcholine, serotonin, dopamine, and norepinephrine as transmitters. They all start in the brainstem, converging in the basal forebrain (important for its cholinergic system in synaptic plasticity, learning, and memory) or the thalamus (see figure 9); they overlap, cooperate, and guard against system failure. In parallel to this, the autonomic nervous system makes homeostatic adjustments routinely and accordingly in physiological systems: coordinating reproductive, urinary, respiratory, and cardiovascular functions, without interference and instruction from the conscious mind. The autonomic nervous system is made up of the parasympathetic system, which relates to the "rest-and-digest mode," and the sympathetic system, which relates to the "fight-or-flight response" (see figure 10), and it is the balance between the two systems that drives homeostasis. Changes in the gut, cardiovascular system, and respiration always occur with emotional behaviors, since those emotional behaviors rest on endocrine and autonomic adaptations. For instance, in a state of fear or anger, heart rate and blood pressure increase, while in a state of depression, they stay the same or decrease.

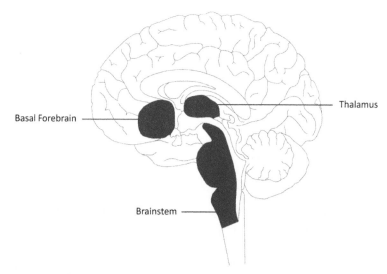

Figure 9: The brainstem, thalamus, and basal forebrain are involved in arousal mechanisms.

THE AUTONOMIC NERVOUS SYSTEM

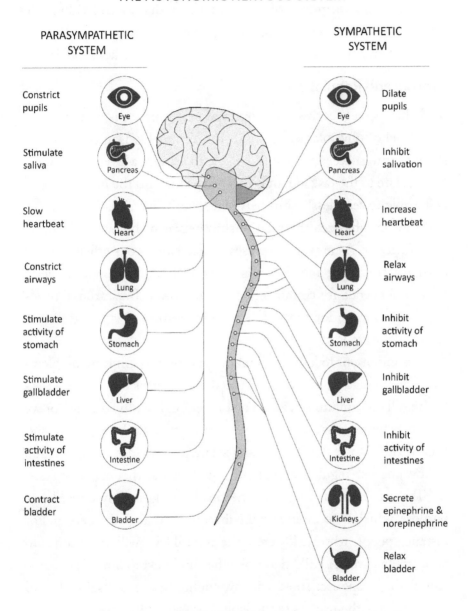

Figure 10: The autonomic nervous system, made up of the parasympathetic and sympathetic divisions.

FROM CLIENT TO CLINICIAN

Thus, it made sense when the course taught us to think of arousal in terms of a continuum of different states that an individual can experience: coma, deep sleep, feeling drowsy, feeling relaxed, being wakeful, being attentive, being agitated, feeling panicked, and so on.

Arousal and Regulation

It has been theorized that optimal performance is a function of one's level of physiological arousal. The Yerkes-Dodson law (1908)[44] states that to succeed, one must be able to achieve a level of readiness appropriate to the task at hand. This brings forward the importance of being able to seamlessly shift between states when situations change, and thus emphasizes the relationship between the level of arousal and efficiency. As arousal increases or decreases, your efficiency will change accordingly, and thus it is all about finding the optimal level of arousal needed for certain situations and tasks. Thus, arousal needs to be appropriate for the task demanded—the key is the ability to regulate our arousal.

It is important to know that many conditions result from problems with the regulation of arousal. Indeed, many of us don't have access to the full continuum or can't stay long enough within a range or we stay stuck within a specific range. We want access to the right amount; thus, we need to be flexible. The arousal model provides an explanation of how one self-regulates, what one does to get to that balanced state.

The use of most drugs or activities is going largely toward one purpose, which is to moderate the level of arousal of the person. For instance, people who are lower on the arousal level will drink coffee to boost themselves. A child may poke the child next to him to get some stimulating response. Those who are higher in the arousal scale will tend to lower themselves with alcohol or something more powerful, such as Valium.

---

44   Karl Halvor Teigen, "Yerkes-Dodson: A law for all seasons," *Theory & Psychology* 4, no. 4 (1994): 525–547.

The arousal model is a way of explaining the brain's function without the use of diagnosis. The brain's ability to go flexibly between states of arousal, according to the tasks at hand, is what we are all seeking. In simple terms, we want our brain to wake up feeling ready for the day and alert, to not be overtaken by external or internal stimuli, and to turn off when it is time for bed. The arousal model enables us to be free from diagnosis and empowers us to think in terms of the symptoms of the brain and behavior, which reinforces the importance of being aware of the interplay of symptoms. The knowledge that problems are not due to moral failings or deficiencies of the will but rather are a result of physiologically based disorders mandates physiologically based solutions.

The EEG Provides a Window into the Arousal Level

Our arousal levels are determined by the speed and rhythm at which neurons fire. It has been shown that the EEG is a reflection of the brain's activity, and more specifically, its activity in terms of how it regulates its own states. The EEG permits us to observe how the brain manages attention, arousal, and many other functions that involve the cortex. If EEG frequencies can be conditioned like hand temperature or heart rate variability, then arousal regulation can be achieved by directly training the brain's EEG. In simple terms, the brain manages everything by organizing neuronal firings through frequencies, which is what we see in the EEG. The rate of brain wave firing is related to our state of arousal. For example, behavioral wakefulness and alertness have been associated with high-frequency brain waves, while sleepiness has been associated with low frequencies.

Arousal and Neurofeedback

With neurofeedback, we aim to teach the brain to change the proportions of frequencies to change one's arousal level. In simple terms, neurofeedback encourages either high frequencies or low frequencies in someone according to their arousal levels. If someone has low arousal, we would want to increase higher frequencies via reward-based training in order to increase their arousal state to the optimal level so they can perform at their best. If someone is highly aroused, we would want to increase lower frequencies via reward-based training in order to decrease their arousal state to the optimal level so they can perform at their best. Arousal is driven by the frequencies at which the brain fires, and with neurofeedback, we aim to find the frequencies that will make people cope with and feel better about whatever situation they are in.

If one experiences excessive low arousal, they generally tend to request more focus. If one experiences excessive high arousal, they generally tend to request more relaxing. For instance, people with trauma would want to find the frequencies that calm their amygdala and make them feel less afraid and less reactive.

In general, right-hemisphere training, which is more prone to lower frequencies, decreases arousal (calms), and left-hemisphere training, which is more prone to higher frequencies, increases arousal (brightens).

This explanation helped me further understand how the arousal model ensures we consider all the changes, reactions, and characteristics of the human body. Primarily, it explained why the changes with neurofeedback are so encompassing and direct. It took all the neurophysiological aspects into account and encouraged us to look at the big picture. However, there were also many things in this arousal model that left me confused.

A Risky Simplified Version

The questions started when the course listed the common arousal problems found at each end of the spectrum. For example, some of the typical *over-arousal* problems were anxiety, anger, impatience, and hyperactivity, while the typical *under-arousal* problems were depression, low motivation, poor concentration, and sensitivity. Migraines, emotion regulation, and sleep problems were put under *unstable arousal*, while autism, substance abuse, and neurodevelopmental trauma disorder were put under *disordered arousal*.

First of all, as Milo's sister, I found it difficult to fit Milo into this linear/column model. Although ASD was placed respectively, I found it too easy and simple to label autism this way. Second, as a client of neurofeedback, I actually found myself in all of the categories; the idea that I belonged to only one category troubled me. My questions were put to the test when we were asked to do a neurofeedback session on ourselves during the course.

To demonstrate our use of the arousal model in practice, we had to fill out an assessment form to determine where we fell on the continuum and get a protocol prognosis. Of the symptoms listed, I checked poor concentration, inattentive, frequent daydreaming, foggy mind, lack of motivation, busy mind, impulsive, fidgety, hyperactive, easily bored, risk seeker, impatient, anxious, sensory overload, and a few others.

The teaching clinician in the class confirmed these symptoms leaned toward an *over-aroused* state, and the recommendation for me was to lower my arousal. My protocol was to place an electrode on the Cz location (middle of the sensory-motor strip) and reward the 12–15 Hz frequencies (lower frequencies). Since I was already used to neurofeedback (but not aware of protocol distinctions), I started the session feeling confident that I would enjoy the result. However, to my surprise, I began to feel very anxious within ten minutes of the session, and my heart felt extremely tight. As I shared those changes with the clinician, I was asked to stop the session.

That night, feeling confused by my response to the protocol, I called Lynette to ask her opinion.

Louloua: Why did the session make me anxious?

Lynette: You were assessed wrongly. You were treated to feel calmer, as you were over-aroused, but in fact, you are under-aroused, so your body was struggling to deal with being even less aroused than usual. You felt your heart because it was laborious to keep it running. The sensory information coming in was at a slower pace than your usual one, which made you feel uncomfortable. This central low-frequency training was not right for your arousal state. This type of confusion is a common mistake. Don't let that frighten you away from helping people, though, because the response can be seen as a good indicator of the patient's inner state, and the clinician should be willing to follow the chains of reaction and make changes accordingly. It's important that clinicians think counterintuitively and factor in compensatory brain behavior. Your over-arousal symptoms were a way of compensating for your under-arousal state. You usually like being trained at F3 (left frontal lobe) rewarding 19–22 Hz, and this high-frequency and left-hemisphere preference explain why the central low-frequency training felt so uncomfortable to you.

While her explanation made sense, I needed her to clarify why it affected my heart because I was wondering if there were side effects to neurofeedback.

Louloua: My heart felt tight during the session. While I understand that this was due to the wrong protocol, does that mean that neurofeedback has side effects?

Lynette: Side effects are defined as secondary effects to the ones intended. However, with neurofeedback, that secondary effect should be seen as an indicator of someone's internal state, and thus an indicator that a change in protocol is needed.[45] The optimal protocol for someone shouldn't have any secondary effect, only the effect that was intended. As explained earlier, since neurofeedback affects arousal, changes in the autonomic nervous system are to be

---

45   D. Corydon Hammond et al., "Adverse reactions and potential iatrogenic effects in neurofeedback training," *Journal of Neurotherapy* 4, no. 4 (2001): 57–69.

expected, thus your heart. Due to the temporal resolution of neurofeedback, the changes to the autonomic nervous system happen immediately, often even before changes in mood or behavior, and thus those changes should be seen as indicators of whether we are on the right path. It is important to note that the intended and secondary effects will always depend on the individual: one person could get some secondary effects, and others wouldn't, as this would depend on the person's original state, what he is seeking, and what state he enjoys being in. The power of neurofeedback is safe to use because it is reversible and offers so many options. Thus, when a secondary effect shows up, neurofeedback allows you to change the protocol accordingly to only obtain the desired effect. With medication, the appearance of a side effect would usually be countered with another medication, and then another medication would be used to counter that other side effect … however, with neurofeedback, depending on the secondary effect that was presented, we have the choice of completely changing location or frequencies, or we can add another location or frequency and end up with a two-part protocol to make sure that secondary effect is either eliminated or desired. For instance, one person may be dealing with anxiety and jaw clenching. Training at T4 (right temporal lobe) at a low frequency should ease those symptoms, as we would be calming the overall system. However, if that person gets to a point where he is too calmed, uncomfortable, and loses focus, we can continue our session with some training at F3 (left frontal lobe), possibly rewarding low beta frequencies for a few minutes to reestablish some focus and brightening, just enough, so he is comfortable again. On the other hand, another person could be dealing with the same symptoms of anxiety and jaw clenching, and, for them, rewarding low frequencies at T4 could provide total relaxation with no secondary effects.

I am referring to them as secondary effects because I don't believe in side effects. It is all just the effects of the intervention. It's like medicine. The term side effects trick you into thinking, "Oops, by accident," but no, you're changing the brain and getting all those effects. Some of these are effects we don't like, and we are causing that. We just have to adjust and make changes. Neurofeedback has no "side effects" in the truest sense of the term because you don't have to accept the "side effect" to get the desired effect. But it can have "incorrect effects"—at least until the clinician knows the client well enough to pinpoint what he/she needs. Everything that has the power to heal has the power to do the opposite, and you need to respect that.

While I was impressed with Lynette's answers, I also felt surprised that I saw a difference between the course's teachings and hers. I had already sensed that Dr. Hamlin knew I came from a different training background than the other students since he was aware of Lynette's unique way of working. However, I hadn't understood that difference until now. Lynette was emphasizing the importance of taking into account a person's compensatory mechanisms and to perceive him/her holistically. She explained that while most of my symptoms were seen as signs of *over-arousal*, they were symptoms of me compensating for *under-arousal* (i.e., hyperactivity compensated for inattentiveness). Through her explanations, I realized that I was being taught a simplified version of the arousal model, and while simplifications are necessary for teaching large groups, they can also lead to mistakes. Indeed, simplifying the complex nature of the human body was counterintuitive.

While I was afraid that knowing the difference between the approaches would be a handicap, it was a blessing in disguise. By the end of the course, I realized my subjective experience with neurofeedback had given me an advantage. I left the course with a recommendation from Dr. Hamlin to intern in a clinic in Boston as a neurofeedback technician. I was ecstatic and ready to start learning.

* * *

I left the course feeling particularly intrigued by Lynette's understanding of arousal. Her explanations and guidance felt more informative and intuitive than what I had been taught. I wanted to know more. I wanted to be fully prepared for my internship, so I requested access to a recording of an introductory neurofeedback course Lynette had taught to educators in a school. I was especially happy because the course was taught at the Step Together Association (the same school in Lebanon that my brother had attended and where I had volunteered). Watching Lynette's course allowed me to consolidate her essential approach to arousal, which is presented below in summary form.

The Arousal and Compensatory Lens by Dr. Lynette Louise

It's essential to start thinking of the core problem and causes of a behavior, label, or diagnosis, and not just stop at what the theories are saying. Acknowledging that dogma, culture, and education can get in the way of a new kind of thinking is the first step toward innovation. We need clear information from people because when you truly understand the core problem, you come up with better solutions, and the best way to do that is to become symptom-oriented. As a field, we are used to compartmentalizing and thinking in terms of diagnosis. However, a brain is a brain, and finding reason and explanations for behaviors and emotions will be more beneficial.

In my experience, dividing arousal into linear columns is misleading and misses an important aspect of feedback loops. I understand that most students want rules to follow because they are easier to replicate than conceptual teaching, and I realize that rules also remove responsibility, while concepts engender it. Humans are created out of chaos, and our assessment process should follow the complexity of the brain, its wellness, and its disorders. Practitioners will only be able to coincidentally help their patients if they apply a model that states meltdowns are high arousal and migraines are low arousal because dichotomous thinking is only sometimes true. Most importantly, compensatory behaviors, such as the way ADHD children become hyperactive[46] because it helps them concentrate, need to be taken into account in the arousal model.

My background is in raising special needs children, home training them before becoming a clinician, and having the freedom to try things. I've traveled the world to work in various cultures under diverse contexts—from huts to palaces. This breadth of clinical experience has allowed me to see beyond the shackles of the field's methods. I followed what worked rather than what was supposed to work, and this freedom led to many adjustments in the neurofeedback arousal model. I define the arousal and compensatory lens as an investigative method to discover the cause of a behavior.

Behavior through the Arousal and Compensatory Lens

The way I redesigned the arousal model is by illustrating it as a circle, rather than columns. The circle brings "balance" into the core of the illustration, and it brings awareness to our goal. In this circular model, we find the balanced-arousal symptoms at the bottom center, the over-arousal symptoms and the under-arousal symptoms at each side of the balanced-arousal area, and the super over-arousal and super under-arousal symptoms at the top, respectively, presenting as compensatory mechanisms (see figure 11).

---

46   Sydney S. Zentall and Thomas R. Zentall, "Optimal stimulation: a model of disordered activity and performance in normal and deviant children," *Psychological Bulletin* 94, no. 3 (1983): 446.

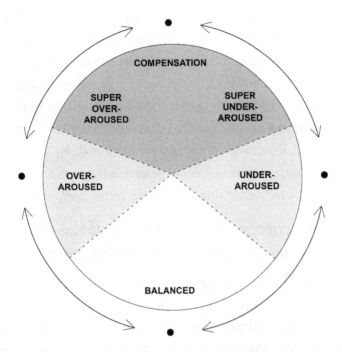

Figure 11: The arousal and compensatory lens by Dr. Lynette Louise.

The purpose of the circle is to show that once you're in a compensatory region, a symptom that looked like over-arousal can be the same symptom as what was actually under-arousal. Representing the arousal and compensatory lens as a circle envelopes the complexities of our human nature and, importantly, demonstrates how and why we should look at a person holistically. It asks the question: how do you self-regulate? The circle shows that one can shift from a balanced state to an under- or over-arousal state, and vice versa, thus establishing the shifting nature of humans. Indeed, we are always trying to reach a place of inner balance, and having that as part of the model will lead to better questions and thus better answers. We are always trying to reach a balanced state of arousal. In every cell, there is a drive for homeostasis, a drive for control. The point of watching behavior and habits is that we want to see how a person self-regulates: how does one continuously rebalance in an attempt to reach homeostasis?

Understanding that behaviors emanate from a place of reaching out for balance, that behaviors are not without reason, will enable us to properly assess someone. Shifting between states is common and natural for everyone; however, things become problematic when arousal states are confused and wrongly identified. This circular model is here to enlighten people on the idea that they could be misinformed about a person's original state and that they could be making it worse if they are not better observers. Looking at behavior through the arousal and compensatory lens will enable us to understand how one operates.

We compensate to get to balance and thus arousal states look the same.

Humans generally come up with coping solutions or self-medication habits. For example, carrying a thermos filled with diluted green tea can be an all-day healthy approach to consuming caffeine for brain stimulation. Or a person with ADHD can rely on chewing gum to initiate brain stimulation. It took years and several evidence-based studies to understand the use of gum for stimulation, and now many schools allow ADHD children to chew gum for focus, especially during state testing. In children with ADHD, the brain is similar to a tired truck driver who is chewing ice to stay awake. In the original arousal model, the behavior of teeth grinding was believed to emanate from a state of high arousal, presumably because the person grinding their teeth looked angry. When therapists discovered cases with brain states that indicated a state of lowered arousal, confusion ensued. The main discrepancy is in part due to our humanness. People are driven to adapt socially and have learned to regulate themselves enough to fit in, and thus, they can look different externally than they are feeling internally. Since neurofeedback gives us a way to look at physiological behavior and ascertain what is happening internally, adding that information of compensation to the concept of arousal clears up the confusion and prevents the client from fooling themselves or the therapist.

We compensate in order to reach a state of inner balance. The drive and reason for nature giving you the method for compensation is the desire to be balanced. We use compensatory habits as ways to auto-regulate ourselves because we end up getting too under- or over-aroused. Chewing, grinding, biting are all ways of compensating for feeling too under- or over-aroused.[47]

In figure 11, compensation is shown in the dark-gray area on top of the "super over-aroused" and "super under-aroused" areas. The graph illustrates that when someone looks like they are over-aroused, they might actually be under-aroused but compensating. For example, someone who is waking up all through the night, might think to themselves, *Oh I just need to relax,* when in fact, their problem is that they are too relaxed. As a result, the person may think, *I need to relax, so let me turn off more lights*; however, he/she would be working against themselves and would be better off getting up for a short walk. Understanding one's core problem will provide better solutions.

The issue is that things aren't black and white. For example, anger is usually considered an over-arousal symptom. But anger can originate from being under-aroused as well. Just think of the number of times you yelled at someone because you were overtired. We want to read someone's behavior rather than their diagnosis or presentation alone. However, people are often taken at face value, and the child who doesn't want to leave the couch is called "lazy," while the one that runs nonstop is called an "energizer bunny." Meanwhile, they may not be as they appear; they might actually be the opposite.

In my experience, the extremely cognitively challenged person who tries not to move, who doesn't want to leave the couch, who wants to be inactive, is most often over-aroused. If their brain is functioning in a too-high arousal state, they might be talking very fast: the sound will be coming in very fast, and they will understand everyone around

---

47   Donald W. Fiske and Salvatore R. Maddi, *Functions of Varied Experience* (Belmont: Dorsey Press, 1961).

too fast. Understanding too quickly may not seem like a problem. However, it means that everyone else is too slow for them, repeats too often, and becomes boring, so they start daydreaming. They resist moving too much because it can flip them into anxiety by increasing the arousal of their already over-aroused state. So, this child may be fully involved and totally busy with the job of trying to maintain an acceptable level of calmness. They may be avoiding anything that will expose or hype them up and cause them to react externally with the anxiety that they are perpetually immersed in internally. This child is the opposite of what they appear to be. On the other hand, if a child is in a very low state of arousal, they will have difficulties processing sound and keeping up with the speed of information flow in their environment. This may develop into a timing issue, so now they avoid people because it is too difficult to engage in a communicative back and forth. This usually leads to everyone calling them antisocial. However, their soul is social, they are just feeling uncomfortable around people at this moment. A person with an under-aroused brain will often want to control the environment around them to slow down what's going on.

As we've explained, compensatory behaviors are attempts at rebalancing.[48] If someone is over-aroused, their heart may race and they may want to try to sit and be still to reduce their level of arousal—they look lazy even though they are burning calories at a remarkable rate. If someone is under-aroused, they may want to try to stimulate their brains and bodies through movement. However, the picture presented by the external behavior of that person appears to look like the opposite of the actual issue: the over-aroused presents itself as under-aroused, and the under-aroused presents itself as over-aroused.[49] Understand-

48   Julia Geissler et al., "Hyperactivity and sensation seeking as autoregulatory attempts to stabilize brain arousal in ADHD and mania?" *ADHD Attention Deficit and Hyperactivity Disorders* 6, no. 3 (2014): 159–73.

49   Ulrich Hegerl and Tilman Hensch, "Why do stimulants not work in typical depression?" *Australian & New Zealand Journal of Psychiatry* 51, no. 1 (2017): 20–22.

ing that overlap is crucial, and that's where the confusion generally happens. Symptoms of high and low arousal may overlap and end up looking the same.

The answer lies in the details, climb, and wholeness of the situation.

To differentiate between the two states of arousal, it's important to look at the climb of how someone got to those behaviors and symptoms, rather than the actual meltdown or plummeting.[50] When someone is too low, their journey will look different than someone too high.

Some people will have the same arousal issues but have different solutions in terms of how they compensate. For example, being under-aroused can lead to a feeling of numbness because under-arousal means slow processing speed, so not enough information is getting to the sensory-motor strip. When this happens, the desire to relieve the numbness and compensate for the under-arousal can lead to self-biting or face hitting. This happened with Louloua's brother, Milo; his sensory-motor strip was very under-aroused. However, his temporal lobes were over-aroused. So, he was a combination of both, and his self-medicating behavioral habits helped us to figure out what to treat first. Often people see someone hitting themselves the way Milo used to and assume they are over-aroused or angry. But it's essential to look at the details of the behavior. Generally, people who are over-aroused are more sensitive to pain, not less. Figuring out what caused what requires paying attention to the details.

The journey toward balance or toward the meltdown is where the subtle differences lie, but once there, it looks the same. There are still some differences, but they are difficult to tease out (see figures 12 and 13).

---

50   Ulrich Hegerl and C. Ulke, "Fatigue with up- vs down-regulated brain arousal should not be confused," *Progress in Brain Research* 229 (2016): 239–54.

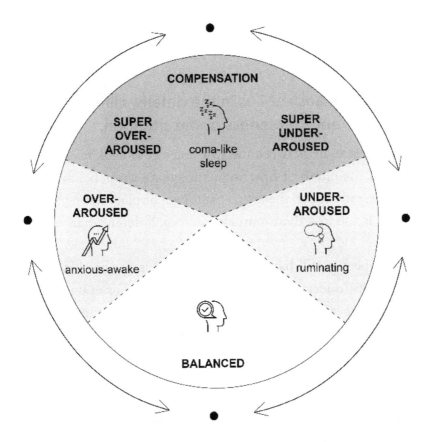

Figure 12: The arousal and compensatory lens as a circle. The example of sleep is used in this figure.

Extreme high arousal and extreme low arousal can both end up in a coma-like sleep problem. Which of the two is causative will be discovered in the answers that the many other symptom questions bring forward: before falling into a coma-like sleep, an over-aroused person would be anxiously awake, while an under-aroused person would be ruminating. Thus, by clearly showing how states overlap, we are shedding light on the origins of some compensatory habits.

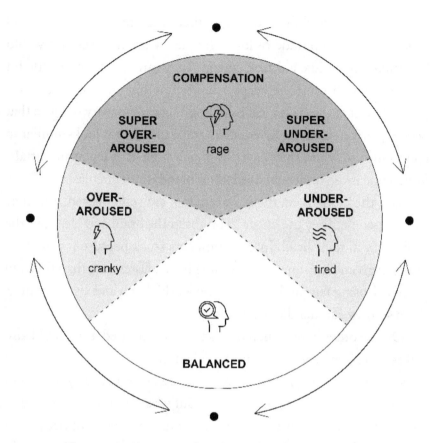

Figure 13: The arousal and compensatory lens as a circle. The example of rage is used in this figure.

Extreme high arousal and extreme low arousal can both end up with a rage problem. Someone who is under-aroused would have felt tired before yelling, and someone who is over-aroused would have felt cranky before yelling. While anger is generally seen as an over-arousal problem, anger here became a compensatory behavioral mechanism used to invigorate the system for the under-aroused.

Let's take somebody who is super tired. Their brain probably would have excessive amplitude of lower frequency brain waves and would be acting almost like a drunk person. They can only focus a little bit at a time, and if someone keeps asking something of them, they will probably yell at them and leave. Yelling is compensatory because that person has too much low-frequency amplitude, but it looks similar in appearance to when they have too much high-frequency amplitude. When one is too under-aroused, their blood is not circulating quickly enough, they look pale, their movements are self-focused, and they snap at people. They use anger to brighten the brain and clear out the traffic jam in their head. Information gets stuck because it can't flow fast enough and information is coming in at a faster pace than they can process. Losing temper helps slow the world down and also brightens them so they can handle what's there.

On the other hand, when one is too over-aroused, they could also yell as a compensatory mechanism. When they are too over-aroused, it feels more like anxiety. Their movements are faster, and they have tight muscle tone and darting movements. But when they are about to yell, they end up looking like they have low muscle tone—not because of inadequate blood flow but because of the contractions of the muscle. They are moving at such a high frequency and are processing so much faster that there ends up being a deficit of information flow. Getting angry slows it down after and resets them. In both cases, they are compensating with their behavior.

Here is another example of a behavior that can be interpreted as both high arousal and low arousal and how we can tell the difference between the two. Two children are running like crazy. The child with high arousal is running to try to alleviate his angry, tense state. He is trying to relax by running because if he runs long enough, opioids and endorphins will flood his system. On the other hand, the child with low arousal is running intensely to try to stimulate himself. He is running like a gorilla with loose muscles and pounding his feet hard into the ground for sensory feedback. The low-arousal child may have paler skin than usual during this problem, while the high-arousal child may have hot, red ears and cheeks. Additionally, his pupils will be more dilated. Indeed, we find the answer in the wholeness of the situation; all the details must be considered together.

When someone is grinding their teeth, do all of their muscles look tight? Or is she grinding her teeth to get stimulation because she has low muscle tone? We need to look at her movements. Are they slow or hyper? How is her skin color compared to her normal complexion? How is her breathing? Are her shoulders relaxed or hunching up? It is crucial to look at all possible clues because the EEG will not always tell us. We need to be bigger therapists than that.

Healing through the Arousal and Compensatory Lens

To be effective as a therapist, it is crucial to keep this question in mind, "Are they compensating or giving in to their state?" Are you reaching a state of balance through a compensatory mechanism, or are you actually responding to a drive from within to do something that you were headed for anyway? Compensation happens, for example, when someone who is under-aroused behaves in a hyperactive manner to induce a stimulated state and reach homeostasis. Giving in to your state happens, for example, when over-arousal causes someone to be hyperactive to release energy and reach homeostasis.

This question is important because once we determine how someone self-regulates and correlate this information with their brain wave patterns, prognosis comes either by mimicking what they are doing to themselves and then shaping it toward the goal or by giving them the opposite of their behavior because what they are doing bothers them. Neurofeedback gives us a choice. In both cases, a state of instilled balance will present as a calm, alert state. However, determining which to go for will depend on how they enjoy being. Indeed, it's important to give the client what they seek. Our aim is to give the client the feeling they like and then work on other things once we've gained their trust. Enjoying the change will reduce resistance and make healing faster while providing us with more information as the story unfolds. We want them to enjoy the healing. If they like the healing, they will keep coming back for more.

For example, someone who is under-aroused and has spent all day trying to stay focused by self-medicating with loud music may have difficulty falling asleep at bedtime. The brain hasn't learned how to move from one state to another. In this case, they need enough arousal to make them fall asleep, such as turning on the lights, reading a story, or planning the next day. At the other end of the spectrum, someone who appears over-aroused due to anxiety might be advised to use deep breathing to help them calm down. However, for some, this could worsen their anxiety because they become over-oxygenated, which increases heart rate and anxiety. And if they were using anxiety as a compensatory mechanism to low arousal and need it to stay focused, even the thought of not having it will frighten the brain.

Therefore, if the client shows symptoms of under-arousal, we should either train at the right hemisphere, which will imply they will give in to the state (calm them) or train at the left hemisphere, which will imply they will fight the state (brighten them). Determining which to go for will have to do with how they enjoy being. We need to ask, what does the client enjoy the most? For example, if the details show under-arousal, but they seem to compensate too much, it may seem as though they need to calm down. But we actually need to increase their arousal because then they will be able to calm down and focus; their compensation method seems to be how they enjoy being the most.

It's important to understand that all this information is still extremely useful even if you don't have neurofeedback available to you. Most of these compensatory manners—rage, for example—are maladaptive ways to get to balance. You don't need to yell at someone to feel better, there is a healthier way. You can say, "Just a minute, I'm going to take a cold shower, or go for a run," whatever it is that can help with your arousal state. Being aware and sensitive to those state shifts will only provide you with better solutions for yourselves and your loved ones. It's when we let ourselves get too high or too low that our corrections become extreme.

For example, if you try to change the state of someone suffering from depression by singing loudly, you're likely to be told to leave the room. However, if you move to the same energy level as they are by singing sad songs, you can gently bring about a higher arousal through jokes and laughter. In other words, it is best to match the state of the person you are with, start from a place of synchronicity, and then purposefully go up or down together. However, it's important to remember that when endeavoring to change someone's state, ideally, we want to go back and forth between balanced and low or balanced and high, not between low and high.

Finally, it's important to remember that we all have a different underlying arousal state as a baseline, which means that we will all have different ways of reaching balance. Let's use psychoactive drugs as an extreme example to demonstrate this fact. The over-aroused may self-medicate with depressant drugs that slow brain activity (such as cannabis) to calm them, and the under-aroused may self-medicate with stimulants that increase activity of the central nervous system and the body (such as cocaine) to brighten them. Both are ways, albeit maladaptive, of getting them back to balance. However, neither understand each other because they are coming from different arousal states. Most probably, if an over-aroused person self-medicated with stimulants, they would get extremely anxious, and if an under-aroused person self-medicated with depressants, they would pass out and fall asleep. There are of course those who are able to self-medicate with both and function; however, there will always be a preference toward what state they enjoy the most, and that's the direction we should be taking in their healing.

* * *

Lynette's arousal and compensatory lens seemed more encompassing and comprehensive. I felt like I could easily understand myself and my brother through this lens. It clearly explained why neurofeedback was so beneficial: it helps us get to a proper state of balance in a healthy manner. While the original arousal model and hers were essentially the same, Lynette was more audacious, trying new things without being afraid of certain boundaries. The three main differences I found in her arousal and compensatory lens were:

1. Consider compensatory habits.

2. Consider the overlap of arousal states.

3. Consider how the client enjoys being.

I couldn't wait to get to work and learn in Boston. You may be wondering why I didn't start working with Lynette from the beginning. She encouraged me to learn independently in a clinical setting with other practitioners, away from her. She insisted that I discover the field, learn from others, and only then determine how I wanted to work in the long run. My time in Boston would be my first clinical experience with neurofeedback and my first exposure to different therapists. As Lynette predicted, I would soon discover that there are many different approaches to neurofeedback.

TAKEAWAYS

❖ The arousal model is a way of explaining behavior and brain function. The model empowers us to think in terms of the symptoms of the brain and behavior, rather than diagnosis, and this reinforces the importance of being aware of the interplay of symptoms.

❖ We can define optimal functioning as the brain's ability to go flexibly between states of arousal, according to the tasks at hand. It has been shown that the EEG is a reflection of the brain's activity and so provides a window into a person's arousal level. The relationship between the level of arousal and performance efficiency is important. As arousal increases or decreases, efficiency changes accordingly. It is all about finding the optimal level of arousal needed for certain situations and tasks.

❖ In the central nervous system, the brainstem's primitive neuronal system activates our brains and behaviors, and many arousal mechanisms are in place to make shifts to our arousal levels accordingly. Arousal physically manifests in three ways:

1. behavior

2. activation of the electrical activity in the cerebral cortex, which usually correlates to behavior

3. activation of pathways in the autonomic nervous system, which sometimes correlates with behavior or EEG

❖ Neurofeedback works with the arousal model by using reward training to encourage high frequencies or low frequencies according to the person's arousal levels. If someone has low arousal (generally experienced as needing more focus and energy), we want to increase their arousal by encouraging high frequencies. If someone is highly aroused (generally experienced as needing to relax), we want to decrease their arousal by encouraging low frequencies. We work to reach the individual's optimal level for him/her to perform at his/her best.

❖ The Arousal and Compensatory Lens by Dr. Lynette Louise:
  ◦ Looking at behavior through the arousal and compensatory lens:
    ▪ We should become symptom-oriented, rather than diagnosis-oriented. Internal states explain external behaviors—we want to read someone's behavior. It is an investigative method to discover the cause of a behavior.
    ▪ We are always trying to reach a place of inner balance. The point of watching behavior is that we want to see how a person self-regulates: how does one continuously rebalance in an attempt to reach homeostasis?
  ◦ We compensate to get to balance and thus arousal states look the same:
    ▪ Humans generally come up with coping solutions, compensatory and self-medication habits, as ways to reach homeostasis.
    ▪ Compensation happens, for example, when someone who is under-aroused behaves in a hyperactive manner to induce a stimulated state and reach homeostasis.
    ▪ However, the picture presented by the external behavior of that person appears like the opposite of the actual issue: the over-aroused presents itself as under-aroused, and the under-aroused presents itself as over-aroused.
  ◦ The answer is in the details, climb, and wholeness of the situation:
    ▪ To differentiate between the two states of arousal, it's important to look at the climb of how someone got to those

behaviors and symptoms, to look at the wholeness of the situation, rather than the actual meltdown or plummeting.

- Healing through the arousal and compensatory lens:

    - Ask yourself: are they self-medicating or giving in to their state?

    - With neurofeedback, we either do the opposite of how the client is operating or strengthen their form of self-medication.

    - Give the client what they seek so they enjoy their healing.

    - We should reach for balance instead of taking our state up and down.

CHAPTER 8

Different Paths up the Mountain

Moving to Boston was a big change for me, and I was ready to give it my all to learn and grow as a neurofeedback clinician. This clinic was famous in the United States for its treatment of mental trauma and offered many different therapies to children and adults. It's also known for its extensive research efforts led by many specialists in the field of trauma and neurofeedback. I was first assigned to work on the completion of a study researching the effects of EEG neurofeedback on children with at least two types of trauma (physical abuse, sexual abuse, neglect, or separation). We were told to follow specific, identical protocols for all the children during the course of the study. While this is normal in research, it seemed counterintuitive to me since I had learned that all brains are different, and individualized protocols were paramount in healing.

As time went on, I worked hard to build my credibility and professionalism among the clinicians, and I took every chance I could to learn. At first, I was given statistical work, assessments, and data entry: coordinating all time-point assessments and organizing and analyzing the EEG data collected. However, I was itching to get involved in the neurofeedback sessions, so I asked to assist whenever possible. After showing my capabilities, I was allowed to do sessions with the children on my own under supervision. I was balancing the research and clinical world as much as I could, and it was interesting to note how different they were. My favorite and most anticipated hour of the week was our weekly supervision call, which included Dr. Ed Hamlin and other clinicians who were part of the study. We had to report the children's states, determine if any protocol changes were needed, and ask any questions. Since I was so eager to learn, I took in every word I was told and asked as many questions as I could. My learning was exhilarating, and the more time went on, the more I understood what my late grandfather used to say: "The more you know, the less you know."

The team at the clinic supported me, and I couldn't be more grateful for all the opportunities I was given. I was surrounded by brilliant practitioners and felt inspired every day. The clinic's leaders, the clinicians, the interns, and the volunteers all worked hard to attain their goals while respecting one another.

Clinical Diagnostic Approach versus Holistic Thinking

While my learning was exponential, I couldn't help comparing it to my experience of neurofeedback with Lynette and Milo. I soon realized that Lynette's approach was different from the standardized approach I was seeing in the clinic and in the literature I was reading.

Clients would generally come in between one and three times per week for a neurofeedback session that lasted 5–30 minutes, depending on the case. The choice of protocol relied heavily on the qEEG (quantitative electroencephalography) analysis and the client's diagnosis. The clinic required clients to see a therapist, and in this sense, their sessions didn't include much behavioral feedback. The roles were well distinguished, and the team communicated well. During the session, the client was asked to focus intensely on the game (which was highly sophisticated to keep them entertained) and the points earned, while the therapist focused on the EEG changes and controlled the thresholds (used to set the reward and inhibit frequencies providing feedback). Therapists shared the behavioral and EEG changes with their supervisor, but the focus was mainly on the changes in EEG seen during and after the session. Talks around the clinic were generally based on the diagnosis of a client, and thus, we were taught about the effect diagnosis can have on a person.

With Lynette, however, I had never done a qEEG , and she had never asked me to focus solely on the game; she was always more focused on my behavior during and after the session, while also looking closely at the EEG. I noticed the behavioral results of the study were not as amazing as the results I'd seen with Lynette, and the children didn't seem as happy or as comfortable. I was given more generalized textbook answers to my questions regarding the children's change and behavior compared to Lynette's more detailed and holistic responses.

All these discrepancies seemed to point to the fact that it was Lynette's approach that made neurofeedback so beneficial and positive. While I was learning a tremendous amount at the clinic, I still felt confused when I compared it to my own experience. While Lynette insisted that I work elsewhere, I still wished I could travel around with her and hide in her suitcase. My comparison to Lynette doesn't mean I thought the clinic was doing anything wrong—everything they did was justified and correct. I was just accustomed to a more enjoyable and holistic healing process. Over time I saw the stark difference between Lynette's more audacious approach and the clinics' more cautious one. These discrepancies made me realize that there were different approaches to mental health, understanding behavior, and doing neurofeedback.

A few months later, while I was still working at the clinic, Lynette came to Boston for a short visit and offered me the first step into genuinely grasping how her understanding of people made her work different from the rest of the field. During her visit, I bombarded her with questions, and each answer I received was relatable and based on physio-psychological information.

Louloua: I was taken aback by the extensive use of the word "traumatized" and the effect it has on people. I even heard someone say the children looked "dead" on the inside. Is that really the result of trauma?

Lynette: Well, you can't really be dead on the inside without being literally dead, so that is just an interpretation of their experience. People can disassociate or pull inward. They can numb their sensory input or over-focus on it, but dead is dead. Be careful what words you use about your clients; your words inform your choices.

So, let's look at reality. The brain often responds to trauma by bathing the brain in slow waves. This helps with disassociation, like a brain airbag for safety at the time of impact. Afterward, you need to deflate the airbag. These children aren't dead inside, they are protected by an airbag composed of delta waves. And that airbag comes out again whenever they feel at risk. When they don't feel at risk, either from within or without, they reconnect. Watch them in different situations, and you will see them come alive. This is the advantage of being a home therapist. I see this everywhere, even in war-torn countries. When you bring children into a clinic where everyone perceives them as dead on the inside, they (and you) will respond in a way that encourages disassociation. At this point, all the neurofeedback and responding behavioral choices will reflect this thinking. Thus, the therapists and the clients will make incorrect choices that then prove them to be right by effectively encouraging the state of being dead inside. This is important to understand if you don't want to help in the process of murdering their insides by seeing them as dead. There is no "dead inside." They're acting different with you and employing the airbag because you are looking at them with sadness. Even if you don't speak about their traumatic incident, thinking about it is audible for these children because they are hypersensitive to energy shifts and know you are aware of their story. In other words, when they feel your energy, they think of their story. Thus, your opinion can lead to them being repeatedly traumatized. Stop bringing up or thinking about them or about their trauma and help them build a future. Understand that by gathering to discuss them with sadness, you are complicit. When an entire clinic filled with therapists expects a child to feel "dead inside," they lower their bar of what is called success. Then they perceive simple cooperation as progress. It is easy to trick yourself into thinking you are doing good work by inventing a dire circumstance that doesn't really exist and then improving on that. Don't do that. Help them feel happy. If you are going to do this work, do good work with a satisfactory end goal in mind.

In my opinion, the current beliefs on trauma are opposite to the facts. Trauma isn't necessarily over-arousal. As long as they think it is, they will treat accordingly, and when what they do doesn't work, they will make it worse by using that same erroneous arousal-based thought process to correct. Remember, trauma bathes the person in low-frequency delta waves to cushion the impact. Even if he ends up with over-arousal, the core of the problem is likely under-arousal, accompanied by a lack of activity in the traumatized brain regions.[51] Trauma victims often resemble patients suffering from anxiety mixed with depression. Many professionals I know think the constant presence of anxiety leads to depression. I believe that often, it is depression that leads to anxiety.[52] Fortunately, with neurofeedback, as long as you target both in each session, you don't need to know what came first.

Louloua: Are labels such as *diagnosis* misleading?

Lynette: We need labels, and yet they are misleading.[53] The first problem with most labels is that they are behaviorally assessed and open

51 B. Rothschild, *The Body Remembers, Volume 2: Revolutionizing Trauma Treatment* (New York: WW Norton & Company, 2017).

52 Ned H. Kalin, MD, "The Critical Relationship between Anxiety and Depression," *The American Journal of Psychiatry*, May 1, 2020, doi.org/10.1176/appi.ajp.2020.20 030305.

53 Amorette Perkins et al., "Experiencing mental health diagnosis: a systematic review of service user, clinician, and carer perspectives across clinical settings," *The Lancet Psychiatry* 5, no. 9 (2018): 747–764.

to interpretation. The second problem is that when a list of symptoms is run through a therapist's perceptive reasoning, it leads to myths based on truths. For example, if a child pulls away because they are sensitive to smells, and the therapist has bad breath, they may think the child pulled away because they were traumatized. Then they may tell people that trauma victims don't like to be approached head-on. The person you tell may challenge this by approaching the child head-on, but then do it with trepidation. The child receives this trepidation as suspicious behavior and then pulls away. VOILA! A myth is born. Another problem with labels is that the symptoms associated with the label are often a diversion that makes therapists and parents blind to a bigger truth. For example, I have a friend that had been diagnosed with bipolar disorder and was on a mood enhancement regimen that would kill a horse. He had a breakdown and ended up hospitalized. They rediagnosed him with post-traumatic stress disorder and gave him a different cocktail of drugs. This helped for a short bit, and then he was again on the edge of suicide and ready for the hospital. I knew the family and their particular creative bent. All of his many brothers appeared to have varying levels of ADHD mixed with a challenging childhood and an artist's proclivities. He appeared the most afflicted. I asked them to give me a chance to help him. Using neurofeedback, I treated him for ADHD while he titrated off of all prescription and nonprescription drugs. We set up daily creative brainstorming sessions and encouraged physical activity. He felt 85% better but still had occasional bouts of anxiety, for which I suggested he use a small alpha stim unit (a wearable device that sends tiny electric currents through earclips by increasing the frequency of alpha waves in the brain). He has been independent and emotionally healthy for several years now, with no regression and no medication. Because of his bipolar diagnosis, no one looked at his childhood trauma. Then, because of his trauma, no one looked at his brain state of origin. The need to think in terms of labels is the problem. If you take the label seriously, you're ignoring the initial wiring, the genetic code, and the past. Labels are a good way to start helping, they are fine as long as no one thinks, "This is the answer," "This is who he is," or, "He's had trauma, so he will act and feel according to those symptoms." Keep your eyes, ears, and mind wide open.

Louloua: Is it essential to have such a perfect connection impedance? We always spend about ten minutes making sure our connection is spot on, and I don't remember you doing this with us—we would start and automatically feel better.

Lynette: It's all right to work with a not-so-perfect connection and impedance. This is especially important when working with sensory defensive people. If you worry too much about getting a good connection, and you scrub his head a lot, he will feel your anxiety, and he won't like the experience of being there. If it's good enough, then leave it alone and start your session. With special needs, artifacts and movement can always get in the way. He should have a good experience. Then he will come back again. As he gets more comfortable, you can get more concerned with the connection. It is true that the signal attenuates through bone and is also contaminated by hair product and interference from some electronics, phones, etc., so one could worry a lot about that but, for the most part, your brain will filter out the static and seek to find relevant patterns in the brain wave responses. Since only brain waves will shift in response to the feedback, not light or electrical interference, you can begin with a less-than-perfect connection. However, you cannot do your best work this way, so improving the connection is desirable as you move forward.

Louloua: At the clinic, we sometimes do a nine-minute session, but I've never seen you do one that lasted less than thirty minutes. What is the optimal length of a session?

Lynette: Wow! Asking parents to drive their children to a clinic for a nine-minute session seems cruel, not nearly worth the drive. It also seems like one would have a serious challenge to assess benefits in such a small amount of time. A typical neurofeedback session is half an hour. The field was first doing sessions of 40–50 minutes or an hour, with no consistency. Any length of time is good as long as you can give enough feedback to assess change. However, length of time is a major component in the strength of a treatment session, so you want to be consistent whenever possible. What happened is that therapists needed to make money and fit neurofeedback sessions into the clinic model. The field also needed consistency to compare results. Thus, the thirty-minute session was adopted. Then clinicians began working with a more difficult diagnosis like autism, and suddenly, sessions were getting shorter. Some people claimed that they had so much trouble getting a child with autism hooked up that they reduced the amount of time, but others said the autistic person couldn't handle more than fifteen minutes of treatment time. Honestly, the problem is usually with the therapist and not the child. However, some patients are indeed so hypersensitive that, if you don't know how to adjust for this, then shorter is better. I personally aim for half an hour, so my data stays consistent. I like the fast change. If I have time and the child can do an extra ten minutes, then I go for it. I mark it down and watch the changes. If the child does better at forty minutes, then we keep doing forty minutes, and that becomes our new normal regarding time. You need to trust yourself, earn the trust you put in yourself by being diligent and observant, and get comfortable using your power in making decisions.

Louloua: I don't understand the confusion between what matters most—the data or the behavior.

Lynette: The neurofeedback therapist's present confusion on the priority of importance between data and behavior reminds me of the confusion I had as a child over the war between science and religion. I have always believed that both can exist and work in cooperation with each other. I may be in the minority, though. As far as data and behavior go, for me, behavior trumps because emotions and behaviors are what the client lives with and why they came to us in the first place. Often all they need to begin the process of healing is the experience of feeling good. Many people can actually have a lack of experience with what feeling good feels like. If you don't know what that feels like, your brain can't reproduce it for you. If I care more about data than emotional behavior, I may miss a chance to instill this important revelation. The fact is, if you have always been anxious, you don't know what it is to not have anxiety. Many therapists try to elicit memories of happier times for the client to use as a baseline, something to remember and return to when stressed. However, without a physiological intervention, if the client's best memory is still a memory that happened in a state of low-grade anxiety, then their baseline is maladaptive. Thus, this client's goal is warped, and having their happiest memory be one that wasn't happy can be enough to tip a person into suicide. When clinicians prioritize the partial bits of data that we can see, instead of smiles, they miss the person. But we need to care about data too because that is the window to understanding our physiological intervention and gets us better at instilling those smiles. Presently, it is important to remember that data isn't enough. We can't tell if a happy memory was happy via data alone because there are too many interconnected cascading effects that are related to different functions, structures, and neurochemicals. But we can use data to guide us into helping a client become more balanced, and this makes it so that the client has the opportunity to experience a non-anxiety-ridden state of happiness if they choose to use their thoughts in a manner that facilitates joy. We are a team. We cannot force anything. Again, let's be clear, there is absolutely no way we can tell what emotions a person is experiencing by looking at their brain waves.[54] We can surmise. But we cannot know. This is frustrating for neurotherapists who don't have time to ask

54   Ting-Mei Li, Han-Chieh Chao, and Jianming Zhang, "Emotion classification based on brain wave: a survey," *Human-centric Computing and Information Sciences* 9, no. 1 (2019): 42.

personal questions. Thus, these therapists often pretend to themselves that brain wave data is more informative than it actually is, and then they pass that false belief on to others. I have many clients who came to me because their other therapist said that they had balanced their brain waves and yet they were still miserable. The fact is, we can't tell if you have anxiety by the brain wave data. We can just tell you what we see and check on how you feel through your subjective report. If a patient looks balanced but is still depressed or anxious, it is due to the deeper information that we therapists cannot see. The only way to perceive the wholeness of the issue is via attention to emotions and behaviors. The patient is the only one with the answers. This is a challenge, though, if the patient has never felt emotionally happy because it means their answers are uninformed. So, it is our job to fill in the gap and inform them. I teach the client about their brain and make them my co-expert. I tell them about both the numbers and their behavior. For example, I might say, "Here is what I observe. You talk very fast and have a muscle near your jaw that tenses and jumps as you clench your teeth when you are listening. Generally, those things are related to either anxiety or under-arousal—either way, this is maladaptive. I will check your brain waves and see which is more likely while you answer a few more questions. Oh look, you have an excess of theta waves on the sensory-motor strip, so you may be trying to activate your connection between brain and body. These numbers need to go down, and these need to go up. Let's see how that makes you feel." Once my client feels better, they can listen and learn. And once they understand their state and how to improve upon it, they can help themselves. Most practitioners don't educate the patient on how they are increasing their own anxiety and how they are decreasing it. The practitioners that do share this information have better results. Unfortunately, the more data-driven the field gets, the more likely the intuitive behaviorist is to leave the field. Thus, patients are reduced to numbers and parts, like a machine. Humans don't empathize with machines.

Louloua: Why are they teaching us this way?

Lynette: Because data lends itself to systemized thinking. Systemized thinking is easier to study and easier to teach. Plus, in the past, too many practitioners had fantastic results, but they were unrepeatable, at least with a systemized approach. So, the outcry for repeatable results redesigned the priorities, and something was lost in the process. There is a danger in simplification when teaching neurofeedback. Oversimplification leads to diagnostically based preset protocols for each patient that has a label. It leads to beliefs about normative brain wave behavior that ignores aspects such as race, diet, genetics, and gender differences. But this type of treating goes against the reality of humans and their brains.

People are different, and they are supposed to be. In Kenya, a five-year-old Maasai child is out working, tending to the cows and goats in the field. In North America, five-year-olds are still getting help with butt wiping but are fully equipped to run a video game. You can't compare these two! People aren't a paint-by-numbers set. However, with a generic norm as the base, a lot of people can be helped, so it is tempting to go along with the concept. Unfortunately, though, a lot of people will be hurt too. And hardly anyone will be helped optimally because you are treating the diluted masses, not the individual. As for the outliers, science discounts them anyway. This is the biggest shame of all because the outliers are our perpetrators and murderers. They are also our inventors and writers. They are our problems and our solutions. If you have to choose, I suggest ignoring the masses and focusing on those.

Lynette's thoughts resonated with me, and her explanations sounded more "human" than textbook. Her holistic approach to neurofeedback, but especially her understanding of behavior, seemed to pave the way for how the therapy progressed. Lynette looks at the whole person, who they are and what they like, rather than just using the diagnosis to define them. While no approach is right or wrong, I realized that clients must be treated in a manner that resonated with our core beliefs and in a structure in which we felt comfortable working. Finally, these differences opened my eyes to Lynette's specific approach to neurofeedback that had been so beneficial to my brother and our family. It made me wonder if we would have gotten the same results if we had followed mainstream neurofeedback; I don't think so. It was no coincidence that we were referred to Lynette. Lynette was recommended due to her holistic, individualized, and positive approach to healing, and neurofeedback was her best tool for creating change. Thanks, in part, to that point of view, Milo graduated from university in June 2015.

Milo's Graduation

After three beautiful years of watching Milo become independent, my family and I traveled to Birmingham to attend his graduation ceremony at the Ruskin Mill Glasshouse College. A month before that, I had been sitting alone in my apartment in Boston, watching videos of my brother working at a supermarket during his first-ever work placement. I found myself crying, caught in a turmoil of emotions. I missed my family and wished I could share this moment with them. I traveled from Boston specifically to attend his graduation, and I couldn't have been more excited. Needless to say, Milo was thrilled to see his whole family, and he was proud of his achievements.

It was my siblings' first time at his school, and Milo showed them around every corner. He walked around campus so confidently, chatting and interacting with everyone passing by. All the students and teachers knew Milo, and it was clear that they enjoyed having him around campus. For the last three years, Milo had happily lived with two different local families who were terrific at teaching him social skills and how to live independently. But it was his last host, Soufiane and his family, originally Tunisian, who enabled him to grow exponentially.

Soufiane and Milo became close fast, and Soufiane quickly grew to be a big brother to Milo. Soufiane communicated with my mom almost every day to report Milo's challenges and opportunities. He took my mom's advice and instructions carefully. Most importantly, Soufiane raised the bar even higher for Milo, pushing him further out of his comfort zone.

During the graduation ceremony, each of the students had to give a speech, and Milo had been working with Soufiane on his. The night before, Soufiane asked me to make sure Milo rehearsed his speech, so he recited it a couple of times while I did my best not to laugh at his cuteness.

The next day, walking into the theater with all the other students' families and caregivers was heartwarming. While we all took our seats, the graduating students sat at the back of the room, each one of them looking proud. When it was Milo's turn, he got up on stage with that special unhurried walk and cute grin of his. Milo gave his speech in front of the enormous crowd with a big smile (as instructed) and looked into the crowd's eyes (as instructed) and with pride (that was on him). I felt so incredibly grateful and proud of him. He thanked all the people who contributed to making his life at the Ruskin Mill Glasshouse College such a success before listing all his achievements. His demeanor was so assertive that he pointed at himself every time he cited an accomplishment. He finished his speech by yelling, "Well done!" and clapping.

What brought tears to my eyes that day wasn't his success alone but his genuine happiness and self-esteem. After the ceremony, the college presented a gallery of each student's work and creations along with photos taken during their last three years. Milo walked us to his area as he zestfully bragged. We saw evidence of his adventures, from glass-blowing and weaving to music, mountain biking, harvesting, wood-working, and jewelry making. His favorite accomplishment, however, was his part-time training at the campus canteen, where he'd helped serve lunch every day. All in all, Milo had learned to overcome his barriers to learning, gained new skills, and, most importantly, learned to contribute to the community, with respect for himself and for others.

It's essential not to omit that Milo still had certain repetitive and restrictive behaviors. For example, he continually described past events and inquired about our future travels. He always wanted us to celebrate him and say things like "Bravo" and "I'm so proud of you." And when he was overly sensitive, he closed his ears and hummed. Those are indeed trivial compared to the behaviors he exhibited as a child and teen; he was now able to engage fully in a conversation, express his needs, and live as an autonomous adult. He was learning to organize his world visually, and he was dealing with his emotional memories. Things were shifting ... and it was beautiful to behold.

TAKEAWAYS

❖ Labels can be misleading, and it's important to look at the symptoms and understand what is going on physiologically without letting the label speak for itself.

❖ Be careful of the words you use, as they inform your choices.

❖ Reassess clients until you reach positive improvement.

❖ We can't tell if the memory was a happy one via data alone because there are too many interconnected cascading effects that are related to different functions, structures, and neurochemicals. But we can use data to guide us into helping a client become more balanced.

❖ It is also possible for a client's data to seem balanced when he/she is feeling depressed or anxious. There is deeper information in the brain that the therapist can't see on the EEG, and thus, he/she needs to pay attention to the client's emotions and behaviors to better understand the wholeness of the issue.

CHAPTER 9

Focus on Behavior or Data?

Having grasped Lynette's approach, working at the clinic in Boston became even more rewarding and more challenging. I took another step along my learning journey and was offered amazing opportunities. While I continued conducting EEG neurofeedback on children in the research study, I was also assigned as an EEG neurofeedback technician to clinical clients and was trained to do assessments. Taking on clients for me was critical not only for the experience but also because I was working hard to obtain my board certification in neurofeedback from the Biofeedback Certification International Alliance, which certifies individuals who meet education and training standards in biofeedback.

But the most exciting shift happened when I learned how to perform, analyze, and provide quantitative electroencephalography (qEEG) summaries. Using qEEG for assessment is a growing trend in neurofeedback. The qEEG is a full-scalp assessment using nineteen or more sensors that are analyzed and compared to a normative database. qEEGs were performed on most of the clients at the clinic to measure their brain waves, and based on that, we would get a recommended neurofeedback protocol. I was in awe at the ability to capture so many data points and use them to get a prognosis.

qEEG

However, being a neurofeedback client myself, I had never seen Lynette do that on my brother or me. I watched the other clients at the clinic as they did their qEEG and found the process to be intimidating. I had felt so vulnerable the first time I sat with Lynette, so I couldn't imagine how sensitive I'd have been having a qEEG done as well. I also couldn't imagine my brother wearing that cap full of sensors and sitting still for that long.

In any case, the clinic recommended that each therapist have their qEEG done so that they could relate to and understand what the clients were going through. As uncomfortable as it looked, I was curious to try it for myself and to see what protocol would be recommended—especially since I had already found a fantastic protocol that worked for me, and I was excited to see what the qEEG would show.

My qEEG showed that I had too many high-frequency brain waves and that I was too anxious. The recommended protocol was that I needed to calm with some T3–T4 training, for example. While the data might have technically been true, it is crucial to note that my experience during the qEEG intake was excruciating. Being asked to sit still with my eyes open and then closed, and then open again, left me extremely anxious. While I wasn't anxious about having the qEEG, the process itself made me tense. And even if my data did show high-frequency activity, why did they assume I wanted to be calmed? In a way, I was offended that someone was telling me what I needed, how I was supposed to act and feel. While they told me that I definitely needed to calm my brain, I felt confused because I don't enjoy feeling calm, low, and slow. I don't like meditation, for instance, because it makes me anxious. I prefer to feel bright and focused; I prefer an activity like reading to calm me. Lynette and I had developed a protocol for me: F3 19–22 Hz and Fp1 19–22 Hz—the opposite of what was suggested. I remembered Lynette explaining in the Step Together video how to determine how someone operates. She emphasized the importance of giving the client what he/she seeks, and I related to that.

I tried to relay this to my coworkers, but no one seemed to understand. The data was clear, they said. Since I felt puzzled by all this, I turned to Lynette to get her opinion on qEEGs.

Louloua: What do you think about qEEGs?

Lynette: While I believe qEEGs are great for extra information, I don't believe we should rely solely on the data-driven information they provide. Data is distracting and leads people to believe they are seeing the whole picture, like when the magician shows the audience the box and not the mirror panel. We humans are easily tricked by what is readily observed. When the qEEG is shared, it often supersedes the clinician's ability to observe subtler information in the clients' emotions and behaviors. If we think we see the whole picture, we stop looking for more information, and this is a mistake. Additionally, basing what should be done on normative data is potentially hazardous. For example, I was working in a clinic back in 2006, and the doctor running the clinic wanted us to follow qEEG-driven advice. Up until we got that advice, the client was making great gains, but as soon as the results came in and we changed our approach, the client suffered a seizure. The truth is, normative data is limited by its norms. Most often, we are working with individuals whose brains are aberrant, not normal. They come to us to feel and function better, but they seldom come to be changed into someone with fewer skills. Imagine if Einstein had been compared to normative data, and then his neurofeedback provider tried to help him with his absentmindedness by changing the function in his parietal lobes because they were aberrant. His uncanny ability to visualize scientific thought could have been reduced, and we may never have been blessed by $E=mc^2$. I like qEEGs, but I think of them as extra information, not THE information. There are 100 billion neurons, and thinking we see the behavior of it all is erroneous, so I try not to be waylaid by brain wave data.

Something else to remain aware of is that the brain of the client is in a different state while being measured and recorded than it would be during daily activities. Putting a band of twenty electrodes on the head for one hour with people watching has an effect in and of itself. If the person being assessed is mentally vulnerable, this difference can be quite magnified. For example, I met a thirteen-year-old girl with Down syndrome. The results of her qEEG stated that she had a brain-wide excess of high-frequency waves. However, after meeting her, I saw her pupil dilation and low skin tone as signs that her anxiety may have been driven by a fear of the process itself. I took extra time with her and played for a while, watching her skin tone and pupils. After she relaxed and got comfortable with the process, it became obvious that her brain wave data had been falsely elevated by circumstance. She was just afraid, and this excess of high-frequency waves was how her brain responded to that fear. In fact, when she was feeling happy, her brain was more challenged by an excess in her slower wave patterns than in her higher waves. Thus, the more the previous therapists had tried to lower her brain waves, the more anxious she became in compensating for that slowness. Hence, I like qEEGs but only for clues. And I never treat based on data alone. For me, the client's wishes supersede my personal assessment, especially regarding data. Thus, the order of operations for their program comes from what they want to work on more than what I see as the problem. To create that personalized plan, it is important to look at the qEEG assessment suggestions alongside the client's symptoms and desires. Otherwise, you can end up with stories like we had at that clinic I referred to earlier.

The constant pressure in the field to treat based on qEEG assessments led me to perform my own little experiment. I had my minimally verbal, very challenged adopted son, Dar, get a qEEG. His qEEG was done on the same day as mine. I sent them both in for analysis without the usual histories, and since his last name is different from mine, no one knew we were related. We had both of our qEEGs analyzed, and I set up a Skype call so that I could have the results shared and fully explained. He began by explaining that Dar's qEEG seemed fine, nothing too problematic, though some of the theta activity in the occipital lobe was slightly paroxysmal.[55] He recommended a protocol. The other qEEG, which was mine, was a source of great concern. They found excessive brain-wide alpha, a low dominant posterior alpha rhythm, and signs of ischemia in the temporal lobe. As I heard how bad my brain was, my son, with his superior brain, was behind the monitor, walking in circles, flicking his fingers, and mumbling gibberish. I mentioned this irony to a neurofeedback therapist and university professor who has an autistic brother. She said her brother's brain is also better than hers as far as the qEEG results are concerned but that he is in a group home and functions at the midpoint of the autism spectrum. While this is meaningful—for me, her, and others—results like this are noted and then ignored because therapists prefer to learn from data, and evidence-based medicine relies on statistics, not stories. However, in my opinion, this inconsistency indicates that data isn't enough, nor is it the most important piece of the puzzle. To get the full picture, I prioritize behavior. I have seen people improve the balance of their brain waves and not improve in their symptomology, and I have seen people improve their symptoms and not their brain waves. In the game of mental health, symptoms are the key.

A final consideration is that getting so many sensors properly placed on severely challenged people often requires sedation. The brain being analyzed then is NOT the brain they live in daily. I work in complicated settings, huts and tents at times. I go to the environment of the challenged person. I need a more mobile, more fully inclusive method of assessing. When I first began, I needed that freedom even

---

55 Paroxysmal activity is defined as EEG activity that is of sudden recurrence or abnormal.

more because so many of my clients were extremely poor. That will be the case for most new practitioners.

Louloua: One of our client's qEEG showed an excess of alpha frequency in the right temporal lobe, which the therapist said was associated with the trauma to which she'd been subjected. The suggested protocol was to decrease alpha in that region. Doesn't that make sense in this case?

Lynette: Did you consider that the excess alpha could be a result of a theta deficit? That it could be a compensatory mechanism? Could it be due to a deficit of beta in the left hemisphere?

Lynette was emphasizing the fact that we should help people become who they want to be, rather than help them fit into the norm. Conforming to a norm means we may ask clients to do things or become something they don't want. A person has a preference for how he/she likes to feel, and that person is the only one who knows what that is. This reminded me of a client who was being treated for his anxiety. While the neurofeedback sessions helped him calm down his overall angst, he also expressed that he felt too calm for his liking. He had realized that his anxiety had enabled him to be extremely aware of his surroundings, and thus be astute enough to make the right choices. He then asked for the possibility of calming him to a certain extent only.

Thus, there are consequences to someone "becoming" closer to the norm if that is not how the person enjoys being. This could lead the person to having some sort of identity crisis. I strongly related to this because when I felt too calm and low, whether on purpose or not, I generally would start to question myself and my capabilities and doubt everything around me. Similarly, that previous client with anxiety would have been calmed all the way if they'd followed that norm, making him uncomfortable and resulting in his need to reevaluate himself.

Her words struck me, and while my interest in the qEEG technology remained, I couldn't ignore what Lynette was arguing.

The Limitations of Focusing on Data

While I was aware of this reality concerning the use of qEEGs, I continued my work at the clinic and continued to learn. I was particularly interested in getting more knowledge about the field, where it was going, and who were the leading players. The "client" in me knew in her heart that Lynette was right, but the "future clinician" in me wanted to find truth in what she was saying. To this end, I put myself at the forefront of all possible opportunities at the clinic. Thanks to the team at the clinic, I was given a chance to contribute to the clinic's publication and research team. I learned how to write abstracts for case reports and IRB forms (forms for the Institutional Review Board to ensure the following of federal regulations for the protection of human subjects) for research studies. I learned what it took to write and publish a research paper. And I learned how to write grant proposals for potential research funding. Again, these opportunities were important for me because, at each turn, I was able to draw comparisons with Lynette's work.

During this period, I attended the most important conference on neurofeedback in the US, as it was an amazing opportunity to learn even more. It was hosted by the International Society for Neurofeedback & Research (ISNR). In the three days I spent, I learned from the field's leaders, who shared the latest research in their talks. The presented studies, in part, showcased the effects of neurofeedback on anxiety, ADHD, athletes, and seizures, and the differences between four qEEG databases were investigated.

There were many inspirational speakers there, and I tried to see as many as possible. Dr. Robert Coben discussed the observed hypercoherence in autism and the benefits of mu rhythm training. Dr. Dirk De Ridder explored the different types of neuromodulation. Dr. Joel

Lubar presented the use of LoRETA neurofeedback (Low-Resolution Electromagnetic Tomography to give a real-time 3D image of brain activity) for the management of addictive disorders. And Dr. Bessel van der Kolk exposed the effects of abuse and neglect on central nervous system development and how neurofeedback could reverse the damage. The conference also offered educational workshops hosted by all the different EEG neurofeedback software companies and the ISNR itself. The hall of exhibitors looked like a scene from a sci-fi movie, full of gadgets, games, and virtual reality devices, and I got to discover so many different neurofeedback systems.

My time there shed light on the direction the field was taking and its focus. I was torn between my excitement about the field's innovation and advancement and my confusion regarding what that meant for patients. While there was some discussion of behavior and psychology, most of the talks focused heavily on data, the use of LoRETA and z-score training, qEEGs, neuromodulation devices, and brain-computer interfaces. As fascinating and innovative as this all was, I was surprised to hear so little mention of the participants' healing and life change. The field seemed to be tediously oriented toward data, software, and instruments to help provide a physiological cause for diagnosis and prognosis of the symptoms. The leaders and research findings were telling us to use systematic and generalized approaches to healing and cutting-edge analysis software.

As insightful as this conference was, I didn't leave with a feeling that these concepts and ideas were being associated and built together; I didn't feel as though I'd learned any applicable knowledge other than the need to buy new systems and equipment. Diagnostic labels that didn't mean anything were thrown left and right. I left with the feeling that I needed to heavily rely on analytical EEG software and that, without it, I couldn't do good work. It felt as if I had read a scientific book with a lot of terminology and statistical data analysis. I was aware that this was a research-oriented conference, and it's important to point out that my opinion is not intended to undervalue the importance of innovation and research. However, as a client myself and an aspiring clinician, the discussions were too densely based on EEG numbers, even though EEG numbers are only an exterior snapshot of how the brain is wired. Overall healing was rarely discussed.

All the complicated questions were generally answered with "I'd like to see data on that," which left me confused since I was aware of the difficulties of doing research. That same research is then implemented in clinics, and since I was aware that clinics tend to stick to research-based protocols, there seemed to be an issue with the field's trajectory. Grappling with these frustrations, my mind reverted to Lynette's approach. The field seemed to be relying on data and full-brain EEGs, while Lynette was relying on behavior and local EEGs. I realized that Lynette's audacity in adapting protocols to the individual's needs, instead of staying within the bounds of research, is what makes her unique.

It's essential to emphasize how much I tried to learn from the field and not rely on Lynette alone. I always purposefully put myself in situations where I could explore what was best in this line of work. However, I quickly came to realize an important truth: all approaches can be successful, they all have the same objective of creating change, and they all end up contributing to the client's healing. But I also understood that choosing your preferred approach has to do with how you perceive people and healing, and the way we create change and healing can be client-oriented or data-oriented. I personally love humans more than I love science and data. And I came to understand that I believe taking care of humans is more valuable to long-term healing than relying solely on the data.

Understanding the Field

A month after the conference, Lynette was giving a talk at another conference in Costa Mesa, California. It was hosted by the Western Association of Biofeedback and Neuroscience, and it was called "Ahead of the Wave: Transformative Technologies." I decided going to another conference would be ideal, especially since Lynette would be speaking. It was also a chance to spend time with her at her home in California and to finally meet her son Dar.

I arrived in LA and went straight to Lynette's home in Simi Valley. I spent two nights at her house—just her, Dar, and me—which allowed us to develop a more intimate and familiar relationship. I was warmly welcomed by Dar, and I instantly felt his love for his mom. I tried my best to communicate clearly with him and to understand him. I'd like to think that Dar felt my affection and respect, which in turn made him comfortable with me. I was happy to see that Dar lived in absolute peace and comfort with himself and the world, which is what Lynette had been preaching to us this whole time. Seeing her with Dar reminded me of how she was with Milo. Spending time in Lynette's home with her son allowed me to understand that Lynette's approach was rooted in unconditional love. We talked about our personal lives, and she made me realize essential truths about my life that only she could have noticed and dared to tell me. We went to the cinema, took walks, cooked dinner, watched movies, and shared beautiful moments. I felt incredibly grateful to know that Milo had spent this quality time when he visited. Now I understood why his trip with Lynette brought him confidence and freedom.

We also did a lot of work together during my stay, and I helped Lynette prepare for her talk about her overarching model. After three beautiful days, we were off to the conference, which was a few hours away. Even though I was enjoying our ride through this beautiful country, I used the time to ask Lynette some questions. I now knew there were many different approaches, techniques, and mentors, and while they all worked in some way or another, I was left with questions that needed answers from her:

Louloua: What can you tell me about the field?

Lynette: It is big, diverse, and a little confusing. It works hard to get accepted by the medical community, has lots of evidence-based research, and, like most fields, it's incongruent. It's funny when you notice that most neurofeedback therapists were drawn to the field because they were looking to help themselves. They are themselves dysregulated in some way or another, the good ones and bad ones alike. I truly believe that it is the therapists who treat themselves, that understand the true power of neurofeedback from actually doing it, that become the gifted healers. As in all fields, some think neurofeedback is effective, some think it is strong but too dangerous to be used at home, and some believe there is no hard science backing up its efficacy. The field of medicine is always populated by differing opinions on techniques and approaches. Neurofeedback, this awesome brain rehabilitation tool, is no exception. While there is plenty of research, the research itself is confusing and applies to many different types of feedback. So, the scientific skepticism is understandable, especially since no well-paid drug representatives are talking to doctors and promoting it. The skepticism is wrong, though. Neurofeedback is effective.

Louloua: What do you think about other neurofeedback approaches?

Lynette: All approaches are good and can potentially lead you up the mountain to mental health. However, it is, as all medicine is, still therapist dependent. If the therapist is good with the tool, then the results can be quite astounding. Unfortunately, astounding results are often met with cynicism, so patients and other mental health professionals end up trusting the therapist that gets lukewarm results because this is more familiar. This has also led to constraints in anecdotal reporting and website testimonials. To follow the rules, we need to separate the truth of human healing from the information used for marketing. For example, if a bipolar patient ceases to struggle with bipolar and no longer needs medication, we can share their testimonial but must put a disclaimer stating that these results aren't typical, even if they are. This leads to presenting information in the "expected and palatable way" rather than with honesty. For example, you don't need to be focused during the session, yet for marketing purposes, it makes more sense to patients and professionals to believe that you do need to be focused. Otherwise, it feels less like the brain is learning and more like magic.

Another problem is that to teach, we need to simplify. Yet simplifying nullifies the real complexity of the brain. The field has become confusing as everybody reaches for simple answers. Simplicity makes things easy and helps new clinicians to get started, but it also misinforms. I advise people to be careful about what they learn. Confusion is dangerous as it leads to overly simplified beliefs, which blind practitioners from creative solutions. My background as a mom of many challenged minds, as a patient as well as a global clinician, informs me and helps me understand the complexity even as I simplify the problem to teach and help people heal. This is something many practitioners haven't been able to confront.

Louloua: I often hear researchers and clinicians talk about subjects or clients who are non-responders to neurofeedback. Have you seen clients not responding to neurofeedback as well?

Lynette: NO. I think a non-responder[56] is just an excuse used to justify not being able to help someone. It is true, though, that sometimes people aren't aware of their deficits and moment-to-moment responses, so we have to help them to notice. We usually have to help

---

56 O. Alkoby et al., "Can we predict who will respond to neurofeedback? A review of the inefficacy problem and existing predictors for successful EEG neurofeedback learning," *Neuroscience* 378 (2018): 155–64.

them notice what is working well as much as what isn't. Additionally, we want to help them envision all the work that is being done for their brain. Understanding these things invites the brain to change itself and heal the area of dysfunction. I would guesstimate that 75% of my success is due to my being sensitive to my client. It is scary to let someone look at your brain. In a sense, you are giving your body over to another person; you have to trust them. It's really challenging, especially for people on the autism spectrum. They're dealing with this lack of control over their own body constantly. I've never had a patient with whom neurofeedback didn't work. The effects are sometimes subtle, but it always has an effect. It's a different complication if the individual or the family isn't ready to go all the way, commit to the whole process. But to see no change, well, that's a bad therapist thing. I try all the different protocols, and I think in terms of neuroanatomy and arousal.

I understand that people need different things, so I don't expect that same protocol to work on everyone. We need to adapt to each individual. Maybe that's the difference. I fixed my brain, so I am flexible enough to adapt. This non-responder mentality is also due to the marketing lie of needing to sit and focus. I believe that is why they think it's a non-responder. They make the client so uncomfortable that the stress is nullifying what we're doing. I allow talking, moving, phones, etc. I think it is better to work on the natural brain state, and most people are engaged in these activities throughout their day.

EEG Change or Behavioral Change?

We arrived at the conference and sat in on as many talks as possible. Sitting with Lynette, I got to see how open she was to new ideas, how critical she was of the data, and how she always knew how to associate and create connections between the research and her work. It was also fun to see her roll her eyes when a presenter said something she didn't find credible—comments like, "Children with autism are afraid and don't like affection," "There were many non-responders to the study," and "They refused to do a session, so we couldn't get them to stay longer than five minutes." I loved meeting clinicians and researchers, and it was eye-opening to hear about all the different approaches. However, once again, the emphasis was on data and instruments.

During lunch, we had the pleasure of sitting at the same table as Barry Sterman, one of the pioneers of SMR training. All the clinicians and researchers were discussing interesting studies and results that had been published. Sterman was pleading the case that if there were no consistent EEG changes seen within the sessions, then there could be no behavioral changes occurring. I learned that he is qEEG- and data-driven and doesn't believe in making behavioral correlations with neurofeedback unless there are EEG changes. This was a surprise because at the clinic, and with Lynette, behavioral changes were seen more often than EEG changes.

Sitting with us were also some of Lynette's doctorate supervisors. At the time of the conference, Lynette was still a doctoral student (all of her incredible work happened before she received her doctorate). Lynette was immersed in an argument with her dissertation supervisor regarding her PhD dissertation because she wasn't agreeing to do a proper double-blind study of neurofeedback using sham neurofeed-back or using another therapy. Lynette only wanted to conduct a study where she could treat all of the study participants with neurofeedback. When Lynette and I sat outside later for a short break, she revealed how upsetting and problematic this dissertation had been for her. She explained that she found the thought of intentionally not providing help unbearable, and nothing mattered more to her than doing good work, even if it meant not fulfilling her dissertation.

I saw this as one more example of Lynette's true love and respect for people, and I realized where her priorities lay. Lynette quickly understood that climbing the career ladder meant compromising or sacrificing elements of her work. It was more important to her to do as much good (by her definition) work as she could than to become the most famous clinician in the world. And of course, this explained her client-driven approach. I was surprised by the remarks by Sterman and others, so I asked Lynette a few questions during the break for further clarification:

Louloua: Why do you find focusing on data misleading?

Lynette: In the brain, there are pyramidal neurons that generate the EEG we see when we are doing neurofeedback. But they are not the only neurons firing. They are what we have to work with, but they are not everything we affect. Through feedback loops and connectivity within networks, we affect the whole brain. We even affect the cerebellum, which doesn't generate any EEG at all. So, we only see some of the data. It is important not to fall into the trap of believing you see it all. We're not getting all the knowledge possible by looking at the brain wave data exclusively, and this applies to all problems in medicine. Here is another example. If the problem is being generated in the limbic system, the cortical EEG doesn't show the actual problem. Instead, it shows us the effect it had on the pyramidal neurons, which have feedback loops going to and from the rest of the brain.

So, simply put, we don't see it all. We see some and surmise the rest. Right now, many clinicians in the neurofeedback field are focused on data alone. They have gotten so immersed in the data that they have forgotten about the lack of information, the information we are actually missing, and all the assuming we do to fill in the blank. When you forget you are making assumptions, you close your eyes and don't see the evidence telling you that your assumptions are wrong. Eventually, the problems this blindsight creates will cause the focus within the field to shift again, just as it does in all fields. In the meantime, this is bad for special children because many of our children's problems are not seeable in the cortical EEG, and much of their EEG can look normal, especially autistic children. Meanwhile, their behavior is off the wall. If you don't use behavior to assess and then lay it against the data, you miss the obvious.

For example, I only see the child in the state I put him in. If I don't observe and question, then I will think that is the whole picture. Let's say I wear an orange shirt, but that child has an aversion to orange and it makes the child uncomfortable. Now he is in a different brain state than he was before arriving. I don't know about the aversion to orange. I put sensors on him and see nothing about orange shirts because the EEG can't actually show me that. I might, however, see anxiety represented as high amplitude high-frequency brain wave behavior in the temporal lobe. So, I may be able to help him even without knowing because I can help him relax in the presence of the color orange. But the frequency of that color is causing an uncomfortable feeling in the limbic system or somewhere else for that person. It is traveling from the eyes to many parts of the brain and cueing fear or anger or revulsion. If I know all that, then I will be thinking of the various places in the brain that these visual signals link up with sensory responses.

Louloua: But I don't understand the unreliability of the EEG since we can clearly see a seizure on an EEG?

Lynette: Seizures waves are impressive, that is true. But they are not the only thing we are seeking to find. And even seizure activity is often missed when the person is not having a seizure at the time of the assessment. They are a good example, though, because if you do see a seizure spike and wave, you may be so distracted by it that you stop looking for anything else. And that would be an example of being blinded by the data. When I say that EEG data is not enough and when used in isolation becomes unreliable, I mean simply that it is not the whole picture. And even if you have analyzed correctly, change can be uncomfortable for people. If you don't factor in their response to the unfolding cascade of difference, you may not be able to help them heal happily. I love data, I use data, I just think it should be interpreted with regard for behavior and emotion. In epilepsy, the problem is clearly seen in the EEG through pyramidal neurons. The feedback loop comes from deep structures, and we can see the overall activity happening. However, for someone who has Parkinson's and isn't making enough dopamine, or someone who is dealing with multiple sclerosis, it becomes a more complex picture. With epilepsy, we can usually see an echo of the activity in the cortex, but when the dysfunctional activity is spread out, changing and shifting its influence and there are no focal cortical points, then we need to use all our skills and factor in the wholeness of a person to make a proper assessment and prognosis. We should be doing that anyway, all the time.

Lynette certainly had a point. I found myself disappointed in the limitations of technology. During the conference, I had discovered several portable neurofeedback systems and was especially intrigued by them. One of them was a wearable meditation neurofeedback system that, at first, impressed me. I loved the accessibility of the wearable EEG device and the ease of its in-home mobile application. However, when I tried it for myself, I experienced little to no change. The device was aimed toward meditation only, which could explain my lack of responsiveness. Or was it the way my EEG was being measured by the device? The reliance on data alone wasn't able to provide the system with the full picture. It was at that moment that I genuinely understood Lynette's perspective: if we rely too much on technology, we can't help everyone because of its lack of individualization.

TAKEAWAYS

❖ Using quantitative EEG for assessment is a growing trend in neurofeedback. The qEEG is a full-scalp assessment using nineteen or more sensors that are analyzed and compared to a normative database, which is then used to recommend a neurofeedback protocol.

❖ It is important to look at the qEEG assessment suggestions alongside the client's symptoms and desires. qEEGs are great for extra information, but they shouldn't be solely relied on because:

  ○ EEG-driven information can be distracting to therapists and may lead them to believe they are seeing the whole picture, which then supersedes the clinician's ability to observe subtler information in the client's emotions and behaviors.

  ○ The brain of the client during a qEEG intake is in a different state while being measured and recorded in comparison to the general day-to-day state.

  ○ Getting so many sensors properly placed on severely challenged people often requires sedation or becomes impossible.

  ○ The high cost of qEEGs begs the question, "Was it worth it?"

  ○ Basing what should be done on normative data is potentially hazardous. Normalizing a brain could diminish something a client likes about him/herself. Instead, try to discern what the client wants and what they like about themself, and try to improve on the difficult part without diminishing these parts. Follow the client's wishes and use their compensatory mechanisms to your advantage.

❖ Asking the client, "Who do you enjoy being?" is different than asking, "How can we get you to become normal like everyone else?"

❖ The field of neurofeedback seems to be tediously oriented on data, software, and instruments. However, success can also be found by relying on behavior and local EEGs. We can adapt protocols to the individual's needs and not be bound by the limits of research.

❖ There exists a problem of oversimplifying when trying to teach neurofeedback. Simplifying nullifies the real complexity of the brain. Simplicity makes things easy and helps new clinicians to get started, but it also misinforms and blinds practitioners from developing creative solutions.

❖ A "non-responder" is the term given by clinicians for clients who haven't seen any change with neurofeedback. However, lack of change could be due to other reasons:

  ○ Sometimes people are not aware of their deficits and moment-to-moment responses, so we have to help them to notice.

  ○ Understand that people need different things, and we need to adapt to each individual and use different protocols, thinking in terms of neuroanatomy and arousal.

  ○ It is more important to work on the client's natural brain state than stressing them out with clinical rules (such as focusing or not moving), which could nullify the neurofeedback effect.

❖ Data alone can be misleading because, with cortical EEG, we only see some of the data. We are not getting all the knowledge possible by looking at the brain wave data exclusively, and we tend to forget about the lack of information. If you don't use behavior to assess and then lay it against the data, you miss the obvious. Remember to use the logic of brain science.

CHAPTER 10

The Lynette Effect

It was Lynette's turn to give her talk. It was called "The Interplay between Autism, Tics, Neurofeedback, Trauma, and Chelation." I'd helped her prepare her talk during my stay, and we'd worked hard to find the best possible way of explaining her approach. I felt like I was finally getting the overall explanations that I'd wanted all along, and I couldn't wait for her to share it with an audience. Lynette planned to use data from her clinical work experience instead of the research data. She aimed to show how her way of working, which encompasses all the aspects of someone's life and is opposite to how a research study is built (which essentially controls all the elements of someone's life but only factors in the effects of neurofeedback). She also hoped to show how a research-based approach omitted some important factors.

I helped Lynette set up her presentation in the large room she'd been assigned. The conference attendees filed into the room, and, before we knew it, the space had filled up. Lynette had a huge audience; some people were even sitting on the floor. While this wasn't Lynette's first talk, it was my first experience of it, and I felt especially happy to see such a big crowd wanting to hear what she had to say when my experience at the clinic had been so closed-minded. I listened with rapt attention as she began to explain her model.

Dr. Louise's Overarching Model

The arousal and compensatory lens makes important distinctions in assessment. Many behaviors are a result of compensating for deeper problems, and it's essential to understand that arousal states overlap. Therefore, a practitioner must take a holistic approach to the client, meaning the arousal and compensatory system is applied to all the elements of someone's health and life. Each element of someone's life is a significant contributing factor to that person's current state and future healing, and thus including them in the equation is important. With every case, the practitioner must look at the bigger picture, applying the arousal and compensatory lens to all the following significant elements (see figure 14):

❖ Neuroanatomy (e.g., How is their underactive prefrontal area or overactive temporal lobe contributing to their arousal levels?)

❖ Behavior (e.g., How is their aloof or affectionate behavior contributing to their arousal levels?)

❖ Environment (e.g., How is their calm or anxious therapist contributing to their arousal levels?)

❖ Medication/supplement (e.g., How is their Ritalin or selective serotonin reuptake inhibitors (SSRI) contributing to their arousal levels?)

❖ EEG (e.g., How is their excess delta in the left prefrontal area or excess beta contributing to their arousal levels?)

❖ Response to treatment (e.g., How is their response to treatment [behaving more or less affectionately or aloof than before] contributing to their arousal levels?)

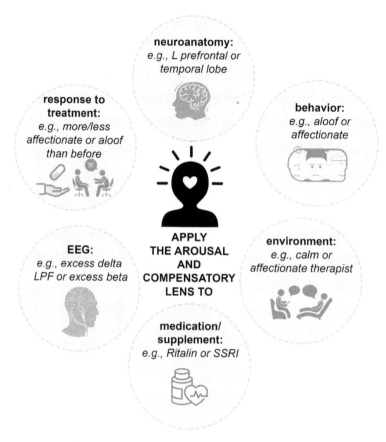

Figure 14: Dr. Louise's overarching model.

Consider the following case study of a child showing improvements before the onset of Tourette's.

Environment: The child's environment originally consisted of two elderly parents, until they separated and the mother maintained full custody. Since she was starting fresh, she renovated everything, from her house to her face and body. She wanted her son to have a new daddy, so she began looking for a mate. She refused all mainstream medicine and educational techniques for her autistic son. She believed the spirits would guide her to where her son would become a prince. She and her son are not genetically connected as he was a purchased fertilized egg.

Behavior: The child could sing fifty songs verbatim, he spoke in scripts (reciting lines from his favorite TV show) using animal names, he had no interactive language, and he was an escape artist, had extreme tantrums, craved sugar, and couldn't use his hands for fine motor skills.

Neuroanatomy/physiology: He was five years old, had a lazy left eye, and had seizures at three years old after taking a vaccine, which resulted in his behavioral regression.

Medication/supplements: He took no medication at all but took a large number of supplements at varying times throughout the time Lynette worked with him.

EEG: His EEG included extreme delta (0–4 Hz) in the left prefrontal cortex and excessive theta (4–8 Hz) in the left and right hemispheres, and centered on the sensory-motor strip. He also had extra beta (18–30 Hz) on the anterior cingulate. After his tic onset at the age of seven (it was so extreme that his neck twisted and his body jumped without stopping), paroxysmal alpha was found in the right parietal area. After excessive chelation, excessive beta and alpha paroxysm was found in the temporal regions of both hemispheres.

Response to treatments: At five years old, he was calmed with neurofeedback and had no more violent behavior. He then developed echolalia (repetition of speech) to interactive language but also responded appropriately when playing. At age nine, he was mirroring Tourette's and, following this, his violent behavior returned, and he had full body spasms accompanied by an extreme sleep disorder. At this point, neurofeedback helped calm his tics (P4 with an alpha reward and inhibiting delta, theta and high beta for fifteen minutes, followed with F3 with a low beta reward and inhibiting delta, theta and high beta), but not completely. After some time, it was discovered that he had been physically and emotionally abused by his after-school helper at home. It was also found that he had been doing chelation multiple times per week from age six to fourteen years old. Thus, the child had had emotional and physical trauma with the abuse and chelation.

After learning about this, his treatments were adjusted, and he now plays the piano to help reduce the tics. He was trained at T3–T4 with an alpha reward, which now calms the tic and outbursts when accompanied with a magnesium supplement and no more chelation. At the time of the talk, the child had minimal tics and outbursts and had returned to school. Presently, he has no tics at all.

This story is meant to illustrate the importance of taking everything into account. If we had just stuck to what was going on with neurofeedback alone, his story would have taken a different route. This story also emphasizes that when treating someone, we gather all the information possible and make an educated guess on the prognosis. But at the end of the day, you don't know what you don't know!

* * *

The crowd was as amazed as I was. The questions coming from the audience showed they understood Lynette's approach. I could sense they were reevaluating everything they knew. There was an energy in the room that seemed to express: "Finally, someone relating neurofeedback to healing. Finally, someone talking realistically."

Lynette is probably one of the few clinicians who includes all the elements of someone's life into her work. It seemed like everyone understood the Lynette effect, and every one of us in the room that day was craving to create their own effect.

Following and Using Neuroanatomy as Guidance

While most people follow guidelines, models, or psychological constructs, Lynette learned that getting stuck to particular models or limiting herself to guidelines wasn't as effective as using her knowledge of neuroanatomy to intuit the needs of her clients. It is the study of neuroanatomy and its influence on behavior that brings her the most success. Lynette's ability to understand a client's story from the evidence presented is the hallmark of her success. It is that audacity to assemble information, create an idea, and find a solution that creates results.

Her guidelines are to include everything in her toolbox, to mix and match according to the evidence, and to follow clues in the client's emotional, behavioral, and cognitive responses. Instead of sticking to protocols and data alone, Lynette "follows" her client: first, the behavioral clues and, second, the knowledge of neuroanatomy.[57] For instance, a child rocking on his forehead means something different than a child rocking on the back of his head with regard to neuroanatomy. While a child with sensory overload may have a dysfunction in his right temporal lobe or sensory-motor strip, a child unable to imitate others may have a problem with his mirror neuron activity.

Autism doesn't follow a model, nor does any disorder; we're talking about unique human beings. A brain learns, grows, and reroutes based on its inner need for homeostasis and the feedback it gets from the world. The power of *following* means letting the behavior speak for itself, and in turn, allowing the person's individuality to come through. While there are many neurofeedback models to follow, picking a single protocol—because that's what everyone else in the field is doing—is limiting, as you can have three different clients with autism respond very differently to a low-frequency placement. However, the common denominator between all the neurofeedback success stories is that they followed behavioral changes due to the brain's response to training. We follow what works as we and the brain seek balance, and thus the brain functions as the expert while the therapist suggests changes to help.

Following behavioral clues will give us a window into how our client is operating. Lynette strongly emphasizes the importance of understanding the brain and encourages us to use neuroanatomy as guidance. Following behavior and using neuroanatomy forces us to think that a disorder begins in the physiology, that a behavior can

57   Bob Garrett and Gerald Hough, *Brain & Behavior: An Introduction to Behavioral Neuroscience* (Thousand Oaks: Sage Publications, 2017).

be understood through the physiology. Lynette urges us to look at the brain through the arousal and compensatory lens and be led by the knowledge of neuroanatomy rather than by science's preexisting thoughts on a subject. Rather than asking, "What do I do with this specific disorder?" we need to ask, "What is happening in the brain regarding the behavior and these disorders?" It is with this framework that we will get our answers. We should find solutions by thinking in terms of cause and effect. We must reiterate that the same behavior in two people can be due to different reasons; therefore, it is crucial to remember the existence of anatomical variation.

Below are two examples illustrating how Lynette uses neuroanatomy as guidance:

❖ The medical community generally treats vertigo (a sensation of feeling off balance) with SSRI—antidepressants—in order to help the client cope and avoid additional stress, which can confound the problem. In most cases, they just think in terms of stress and not stress, or stress and anger, or sadness and anger. However, while Lynette does find value in reducing stress, it would be preferable to correct the problem in the first place; thus, bringing it all the way down to the actual physiology is more beneficial. Let's treat the root cause instead of managing symptoms. Looking at vertigo through the arousal and compensatory lens points to needing more high-frequency connection or a quicker processing time for the area over the cochlea. In neurofeedback, generally this would mean treating C4, C5, C6, or C3 depending on which way your dizziness is turning. So, if the vertigo is going to the right, then we would generally treat it on the right (C4 or C6) with a higher frequency reward (15–18 Hz). Looking at vertigo through the arousal and compensatory lens also points to thinking in terms of what neurochemicals are being released. High frequency suggests dopamine and norepinephrine, so do we have to calm this area because it's releasing too many neurochemicals that would make you uncomfortable, or is it that the area isn't processing and making the connections it needs to?

❖ With Parkinson's disease (a disease that affects the nerve cells in the brain that produce dopamine), Lynette thinks of the effects of dopamine in the disorder: dopamine is stimulating, and since dopamine is failing, she presumes the client needs more stimulation. If she puts an electrode on the dopaminergic pathway and requires the brain to fire more high-frequency brain waves, the brain might find a way to compensate for the reduced dopamine with other neurochemicals. And it works!

Lynette explains in *Miracles Are Made*:

Having the ability to think like a brain detective[58] clears away the confusion created by that mosaic of behaviors your autistic child is presenting you with and can be applied to improve the results of any therapy you may be using. Understanding the brain helps you to understand the details and gives you the energy to continue. For example, if you know why motivation matters and/or why happiness improves memory, you are more likely to use them both. So you see, understanding the brain helps you to understand to what you should attribute a behavior, which helps you to understand how to follow and consequently affect symptoms that show up as behaviors. In addition, understanding the brain helps you to appreciate and comprehend the unbelievable degree to which your behavior can and does affect someone else's brain. This is empowering as it helps you focus on how to behave in order to properly address the symptoms in the person you are trying to help: most likely, your child. Thus by learning how to follow, you come

---

58 Caterina Gratton et al., "Defining Individual-Specific Functional Neuroanatomy for Precision Psychiatry," *Biological Psychiatry* 88, no. 1 (2020), 28–39.

to understand what to do in order to make a positive difference with the knowledge you have. And suddenly, autism is no longer a diagnosis without directions. Add to that an understanding of neurofeedback, which, as you may recall, is merely site-specific brain wave information being fed back very quickly to the brain, causing changes in emotions and behavior to be experienced almost immediately, and you become more convinced of the value of feedback itself. Knowing how feedback works and seeing such obvious change being achieved by a method similar to your own feedback via reaction behavior helps you analyze and intentionalize the feedback you use at home. It also helps you understand the degree to which you, your relatives, your neighbors, and your child's teacher can and will affect your babies [sic] brain.[59]

* * *

Lynette's approach made me understand the power of feedback; the way we assess must be a moving fluid hypothesis. It's vital that the assessment lay on the foundational concept of arousal state and its thought process, and not on simple rules. Understanding requires that all observable and reported information be inserted into the details of the overall story. Neither the child who learns to behave for us and pretends to feel better nor the qEEG are always reliable as our sole source of information. It is from the details of the person's *unfolding overall story* that the complete assessment and prognosis must continue to come.

While I was afraid of the dichotomy between the work at the clinic and what I had grasped from Lynette, I ended up finding a way of integrating Lynette's thinking into my work at the clinic. Now that things were clearer in my mind, I was able to provide thorough explanations for behaviors when my coworkers and I disagreed. Thankfully, most of the coworkers understood my perspective and tried to embrace it

---

59   Lynette Louise, *Miracles Are Made: A Real-Life Guide to Autism*, 19–20.

as much as they could. I realized the importance of making Lynette's approach more applicable to the rest of the field, whether fully, in part, or as an inspiration.

After a couple of months of work in Boston, I had to return home to Paris to attend to some pressing family matters. Before leaving, I received my certification in EEG Neurofeedback from the Biofeedback Certification International Alliance. I thanked all my amazing coworkers, and left the United States.

TAKEAWAYS

❖ Lynette's method is to apply the arousal and compensatory lens to all the following significant elements and determine how each contributes to the client's arousal levels:

  ◦ Neuroanatomy

  ◦ Behavior

  ◦ Environment

  ◦ Medication/supplement

  ◦ EEG

  ◦ Response to treatment

❖ It is important to look at all the elements of the overall picture. Paying attention to these elements will help us avoid omitting crucial information about the client. You don't know what you don't know.

❖ Lynette's study of neuroanatomy and its influence on behavior is what brought her the most success. Getting stuck to particular models or limiting herself to guidelines wasn't as effective as using neuroanatomy knowledge to follow the needs of her clients:

  ◦ Follow clues in the client's emotional, behavioral, and cognitive responses to discover a window into how the client is operating.

  ◦ Understand the brain and use neuroanatomy as guidance. Follow your knowledge of neuroanatomy to inform you about symptoms and pave a path.

  ◦ Think like a brain detective: a disorder begins in the physiology; a behavior can be understood through the physiology.

CHAPTER 11

For the Love of Humans or Science?

B ack home in Paris, I was now a board-certified neurofeedback technician and was adamant about continuing in this field. At this point, I knew my biggest obstacle to my credibility was that I didn't have a relevant degree, so I applied for a master's program in London starting the following fall. In the meantime (I had six months), Lynette suggested I continue working with family and friends in Paris under her supervision. So I became a member of Lynette's clinic on the road, Brain and Body's International Outreach Program Team, and began working with some clients. Now that I was back in Europe, I took time to explore their approach to the neurofeedback field. To my surprise, the recurrent theme of my past confusion was still present: research was presenting one thing while life around me was presenting another.

Science in Paris and Munich

Within a month of my return to Paris, the country hosted its first conference on neurofeedback: "Première Journée Nationale sur le Neurofeedback." I attended the conference and was thrilled to see the big crowd, so happy that the healing powers of neurofeedback were being promoted. The conference was an introduction to the therapy and included many worldwide researchers on the topic.

Dr. Martijn Arns gave a great talk, which mainly pointed the finger at the flaws in the research into neurofeedback. He pinpointed the importance of having protocols suited to specific disorders and individuals, and to that end, stressed that neurofeedback protocol should be specific to what you are trying to treat. For instance, using the same protocol on individuals with ADHD and those with anxiety will give different outcomes, and thus shouldn't be compared.[60] As he said, "You can't compare apples to oranges." He finished his talk by complaining about the EEG gadgets that were claiming to be neuro-feedback and explained how these weren't individualized and shouldn't be considered on the same level. He was calling for the field to under-stand what neurofeedback truly is, to produce proper research, and to create meta-analyses on the therapy. He also reasserted that neuro-feedback is a process of operant conditioning (associating a voluntary behavior and a consequence) and classical conditioning (associating a stimulus and an involuntary response) and talked about the flaws in using complex software neurofeedback games. He emphasized that the feedback games must be kept as simple as possible in order to ensure clarity and to improve the chances that the reinforcing stimulus will increase the probability of a physiological response.

I was encouraged to find that his values aligned with mine. I intro-duced myself after his session, and he told me about his research and clinic in Munich, Germany. They offered a course in neurofeedback in ADHD, which he encouraged me to take. I told him about my experience in the US, but he was confident I would learn different things with him.

When the time came, I went to Munich for the three-day course at the neuroCademy in the neuroCare Group. The course was called "Neurofeedback in ADHD and Insomnia" and was taught by Dr. Martijn Arns and his colleagues. It is a high-caliber course that I recommend. I found it insightful as it delved into the specifics of the learning mechanisms behind neurofeedback, how to read EEG and

60   M. W. Arns, "Personalized Medicine in ADHD and Depression: A Quest for EEG Treatment Predictors," (dissertation, Utrecht University, 2011), http://dspace.libra ry.uu.nl/handle/1874/215188.

qEEGs, and other types of training. While I absorbed all the knowledge, I also grew interested in the neuroCare Group business model. They had built an institution for neurofeedback in the clinical and research fields and were trying to expand into worldwide markets. While there was a part of me that found this appealing, I still had a long way to go to build my experience and credibility. My dad was particularly excited to hear that there was an opportunity of mixing neurofeedback and business together and scaling it.

In any case, as fascinating as this was, I was again surprised to see the dichotomy between research and clinical neurofeedback. The course was mainly based on understanding the importance of EEG and qEEGs, and especially on what research had shown, and I had understood the importance of that by now. I learned that people mainly follow what research had proven, and not what clinical experience showed. For this reason, I wasn't necessarily seen as credible as most of my work was clinical and not research-based. However, what surprised me most was that they asserted that the reward in frequencies in training didn't matter. So, training someone and rewarding either 12–15 Hz or 15–18 Hz brought no relevant change and made no difference. This was asserted because research hadn't proven otherwise, while clinical experience had shown the opposite. I was shocked, to say the least. I had witnessed clients feel nauseous if the reward frequency was too low and clients feeling anxious if the reward frequency was too high. While we clinicians knew that, it seemed that research was lagging behind our clinical findings.

A Client, First and Foremost

While I was working as a clinician and meeting admirable minds in the field, the client in me only seemed to notice the big divide between the realities of science and the realities of human beings. It was true that the professionals around me were passionate about their findings, data, and academia. However, I kept wondering if they ever felt or related to any of the subjects or patients they were studying. Still being the sister of a brother with autism, and a young soul still battling with her mental states, the reality of our human condition never left my side.

Vulnerability researcher Brené Brown says, "The definition of research is to control and predict, to study phenomena for the explicit reason to control and predict. And now my mission to control and predict had turned up the answer that the way to live is with vulnerability and to stop controlling and predicting."[61] Indeed, this spoke to me greatly and explained the dichotomy that I was witnessing between the research and clinical worlds.

I'd like to share an example from my own life. One day I found myself lying on my bed in my bathrobe, in the fetal position, for a whole hour without moving. While my day had started like any other, I hadn't been feeling like myself the past two weeks and knew I should do a neurofeedback session to brighten myself up. In any case, after I had showered that day, choosing what to wear and getting dressed felt daunting. I sat on my bed, staring at my closet, thinking, *How am I going to do this?* Then I laid down and hugged myself. And I was stuck. Getting up seemed to be the hardest task in the world.

My mom came into my room about an hour later and was surprised to find me in bed. She asked if I was okay. And the only thing I could tell her was: "Mom, please prepare the neurofeedback computer for me." She nodded and went to prepare the session. She came back five minutes later, told me it was ready, and helped me to get out of bed. After a thirty-minute session, I felt comfortable enough to get dressed and felt able to go to lunch. The rest of the day passed pleasantly, and it was as if this episode had never happened.

I can honestly say that I wouldn't have gotten up if I hadn't known

---

61   Brené Brown, "The power of vulnerability," TEDxHouston, June 2010, https://www.ted.com/talks/brene_brown_the_power_of_vulnerability/transcript?language=en.

that neurofeedback was waiting for me, and having my mom prepare it for me meant the world. Being able to do a session when you need it the most is an incredible advantage because teaching your brain to change itself should be done on the spot. I'd made the mistake of not doing a session when I needed it. When you start to head in a particular direction, it is a beautiful thing to be able to correct, and it means that an entire trajectory of negativity can be avoided. However, it is during those low points when I remember the complexities of our line of work, and I struggle with the research blindness to real-life conditions.

It was also during those moments that I remembered Milo. I tried to imagine how difficult it must be for him to deal with the world when he wasn't feeling well. I hoped he was well understood by his peers.

Since graduating from Glasshouse College, Milo was still living in Birmingham with Soufiane, continuing his studies in a bigger establishment called Dudley College of Technology. A further education college that was fifteen minutes away from his previous university, Dudley offered a special needs program called Aspire and aimed to teach students employability and living skills. Through the use of an engineering workshop, commercial print room, retail showroom, real-life kitchen, garden, and craft room, Milo was smoothly getting ready for the real world. We were lucky that Dudley College often looked to recruit Glasshouse College graduates because, if it hadn't been for their own interest and assessment of Milo, we would have missed out on a great opportunity. One of the great things at Dudley was Milo's inclusion with neurotypical students at the school canteen for lunch. It became a motivator for Milo to start working because he needed to make money to pay for his food! Finding work opportunities was challenging at first, as you can imagine.

His first "internship" was at a children's charity that sold second-hand goods at a discounted price. Milo was in charge of steaming the clothes and properly presenting the items on hangers in the storefront (since Milo loved to organize). Soufiane later convinced the owner of the hair salon where Milo had his hair cut to hire Milo to clean his shop every Saturday. Milo would mop the floors, wipe the shelves, and clean all the hair-beauty bottles (since Milo loved beauty products). Now that Milo had gained some sort of professional maturity, he later got the chance to work in a toy store. Milo would stick prices on the toys and arrange them accordingly on the shelves, and even got to work as a cashier! Finally, Milo's favorite job of them all was his experience working in the kitchen of a hotel (since he loved food). Milo would wash plates, cut vegetables, and eventually learned how to make vegetable soup! It was thanks to his experience in the kitchen that Milo's interest in cooking solidified. His training in cooking continued at home with Soufiane and his wife, Sana, who would teach him home recipes and how to cook independently. They made it a fun and rewarding process for him as they filmed him and sent us the amazing videos!

We felt grateful that Milo had the support and courage to throw himself out there and gain experience in the professional world. Through all his different roles, Milo learned new skills and eventually realized what he enjoyed doing and that he was good at cooking. He was so incredibly proud of his work, and we couldn't believe the determination, discipline, focus, and calm Milo had while cooking. Milo was a happy young man who was continually improving. His work experiences had given him a sense of purpose and motivated him to keep growing.

I couldn't help but wonder… if someone looked at Milo's EEG, would they only see the abnormalities, or would they take his growth and happiness into account?

This series of experiences taught me how to synthesize what I'd learned from the field of neurofeedback and from Lynette's approach. I learned that I could speak the language of both the research side and the clinical side.

Neuroimaging

With this in mind, I traveled to London for a weekend to attend an open evening at King's College of London (KCL) and discover the different master's programs I could apply to. I was taken by the prestige of the Institute of Psychiatry, Psychology & Neuroscience (IoPPN) of KCL, standing as a world leader in the research, study, and practice of psychiatry, psychology, and related disciplines. During the visit, students were given a chance to visit the MRI (magnetic resonance imaging) facilities that were used for research projects at the IoPPN. Looking at this massive machine, I inquired about what sorts of projects were being conducted and the first one mentioned was a study testing the efficacy of MRI-neurofeedback. I asked what master's program that was for and ran to the booth of the program in neuroimaging.

Come September 2016, I was off to London to start my master's in neuroimaging at KCL. I had decided to enroll in the neuroimaging course, as I felt it would be more beneficial to learn about the technical side of my work, versus the clinical side of it. I was still curious about what neuroscience and technology could create together. Most importantly, KCL had specific funding for testing the efficacy of neurofeedback with MRI machines, especially for the neuroimaging MSc, and so, it couldn't have been a better fit.

Neuroimaging, or brain imaging, is the use of various methods to image the function, structure, or pharmacology of the nervous system. The course taught us the foundations of neuroimaging acquisition and analysis regarding MR scanners, positron emission tomography (PET), Magnetoencephalography (MEG), computed tomography (CT), ultrasound, and EEG modalities. It also explored clinical application to autism, epilepsy, genetics, and strokes, as well as other non-clinical applications such as fetal/baby imaging, neurofeedback, pre-clinical imaging, pharmacological MRI, and neuromarketing. I learned tremendously through this course, especially since it enveloped the worlds of psychiatry, neurology, psychology, clinical neuroscience, physics, and coding.

Neurofeedback played a significant part in the program and focused particularly on real-time fMRI (rtfMRI) neurofeedback. The concept is the same as EEG neurofeedback but instead of using EEG as a measurement, it uses blood-oxygen-level-dependent (BOLD) levels and uses an MR scanner in real time to take measurements instead of electrodes. Thanks to the university's direct access to MR scanners, rtfMRI neurofeedback was growing. I was so excited about this that on top of my class load, I'd asked to shadow a research project on rtfMRI neurofeedback that focused on understanding self-blaming emotions in major depressive disorder and testing the clinical benefits of treatment. It was truly amazing to watch study participants enter an MRI machine and do a neurofeedback session. While I was used to electrode placement, with MRI we could target a specific region of interest in the brain, and we weren't limited to the cortical areas. I was also especially interested in machine learning, which was considered a promising tool for neuroimaging data analysis. It inspired me to think of how we could potentially program a computer to optimize Lynette's arousal and compensatory lens, for example. By using example data or past experience, the computer could make a prediction about new data. Thus we could essentially teach the computer to recognize patterns in our arousal assessment. However, I couldn't help but wonder, *Can the technology encompass our holistic thinking without compromising the human element of the model?*

My final year dissertation project aimed to investigate the learning mechanisms involved in rtfMRI neurofeedback. We were looking to understand at which level learning was taking place in the brain and where. Our results showed that a large network of the brain was involved in self-regulation, and the behavioral data suggested a drop in performance followed by stability rather than improved positive performance, thus implying that learning in neurofeedback is about stabilization and consistency of performance.

My enthusiasm for neurofeedback was obvious. The more time I spent talking about neurofeedback with professors and students, the more often I was asked the same question: "Why isn't neurofeedback more mainstream?" I turned to Lynette for an answer.

Louloua: Why isn't neurofeedback more mainstream?

Lynette: Actually, I'm much better at answering questions about the brain and behavior than I am about politics, and I believe that the answer to this question is political. Generally speaking, I would have to say that neurofeedback has increased in its visibility and its credibility. There are more and more studies on it. There is a lot more clinical evidence. The problem as I see it, is that we raise doctors up in the medical system to write prescriptions or do surgery. This is our main line of defense against illness and anybody who is doing rehabilitation or preventive medicine is sort of in the background. It's not just unique to neurofeedback. Part of that is that it's more difficult to do and it's more people dependent. For example, you can't go to a physiotherapist without having the physiotherapist's attention. And paying attention to each person to work makes it difficult to mass produce, whereas medicine can be mass produced. And surgery isn't a good comparison because surgery has an enormous impact right away, whereas something like neurofeedback requires repeated sessions and requires effort on the part of the patient and practitioner and it requires time. It ends up expensive in that regard at the outset. However, it's cheaper over the long term because you actually get better instead of remaining dependent on medication for the rest of your life and having to actually go from one medication to another medication, and then a medication for the side effects and another medication, etc. You would be in a better place later with neurofeedback, but it's harder in the beginning.

And if I want to talk about the political stuff that I've heard in conferences and such, for example that we don't have lobbyists or that we don't have the kind of support that we need in the insurance companies, then they're probably true. However, I think that a piece is missing when we go ahead and complain like that and don't look at part of the problem being that a patient who is in desperate need doesn't want to be told that it's going to take effort and that it's going to take repeated visits. They want to be told that they're going to walk out of that doctor's office with something in their hand that they can take to the pharmacy and feel better immediately or within five days (antibiotics usually take five to seven days). So, we are fighting an entire mindset when we say, "Look, yes, you could do that, but you're setting up a problem in the future," versus "Here, go ahead feel better now, who knows, you might be hit by a car tomorrow." This is sort of a long-term benefit versus short-term results kind of problem that I think has to be addressed not just in the medical field but in the way that we approach raising children in the first place.

There is a lot of change that has to be made at the fundamental, foundational beginning point where we train, teach, and raise children and professionals to believe that effort in the beginning is worth ease in the latter part. We understand that when it comes to piano lessons or going to school, for example. We understand that learning to play the piano involves more than just sitting in front of the keys. Getting an education takes more than just walking into a school building. We need to teach people that this applies throughout life. We need to change how we approach the learning because most of the time it is sort of forceful rather than playful. We should aim to emphasize a love of learning versus the mentality of "learn or else …." And that difference in how we teach and how we embrace change affects us later in the choices we make. I think that's the real answer to your question.

Searching for the Human Element

While this was all fascinating, I felt like I was missing a big part of the human element and found it difficult to stick to results without looking at the big picture and thinking holistically. Doing a neurofeedback session in an MRI machine is a challenging process, and it's even more demanding from a healing perspective. The behavioral assessments lacked substance and context to me. A research study implies creating a research context, which I found to be contradictory to real-life situations.

This was particularly evident to me when friends and family in London grew curious about neurofeedback and expressed interest in trying a session. One friend was training for her anxiety, and another for his depressive tendencies and lack of motivation and energy. While each session showed results, I struggled to make time for consistent sessions, and work had to stop. However, I found the immediate change created within those sessions to be more rewarding than the research and academic work I was doing at university. My time in London reinforced my love of neurofeedback, as I was living both the research and clinical aspect of it and studying it more thoroughly than I ever had before. Thanks to all of this studying, I was able to truly comprehend why I found neurofeedback to be so effective.

But even more than the research and clinical study, it was my relationship with my husband, Tarek, that expanded my understanding of neurofeedback. Tarek and I had met over the summer in Lebanon, and from the first day we met, I was taken by his honesty, integrity, and kindness. His intellect continues to inspire me day after day.

As we were getting to know each other, Tarek became increasingly interested in determining what I found so fascinating about my work. The more we talked, the more he helped me understand that neurofeedback envelops everything in one: technology, neuroscience, behavior, and healing.

I was over the moon when Tarek expressed his curiosity to try a neurofeedback session for himself. Our first session together was the most nerve-racking session I had ever done, considering that this was the first time I had been in love with the person I was putting the electrodes on. Thankfully, my assessment was correct, and Tarek felt calmer and less anxious within one session. We agreed that feeling the effects of the session was essential in his understanding of my work. After experiencing neurofeedback for himself, he properly understood how it can add value to someone's life.

This added-value concept became important in my life, as it was what my dad always encouraged us to look for. When I asked my father to allow me to travel to Africa or the Middle East to do volunteer work as a kid, or when I asked him whether I should become a psychologist or a play therapist, his answer was always the same: "Are your hands more beneficial than someone else's? What's your added value?" Ultimately, neurofeedback became my added value.

Having those personal experiences while studying for my master's reinforced the power and importance of creating direct clinical change versus focusing on the how and why of certain mechanisms. Studying and being so involved in research made me realize how much more I enjoyed contributing to healing, rather than conducting research. I met incredible people at KCL and realized that each person had their own objective. We were all open to each other's points of view. My experience in academia reinforced my belief in Lynette's approach even more. While some experts in the field are focused on findings, papers, academics, and publications, Lynette and I focused on change, healing, and positive outcomes for clients.

By the end of my studies, I found myself interested in creating change more than analyzing the process of creating that change. As I learned about so many different innovations regarding brain imaging, the course made me realize my objective: to work with something that provides change in the fastest and easiest way, in a happy and comfortable environment. The more time went on, the more I learned and realized that it was through EEG neurofeedback that I could do that. EEG neurofeedback can be done in the comfort of a home or a school, on a couch, with family or friends around, with just a few electrodes, and could be completed within thirty minutes. EEG neurofeedback is a tool that makes our approach to behavior applicable and relatable, without having to lose the sense of the big picture and of healing.

TAKEAWAYS

❖ The flaws and improvements needed in neurofeedback research:

   ○ It is important to have protocols suited to specific disorders and individuals. Thus, when we compare the success of a neurofeedback protocol, it should be specific to what we are trying to treat.

   ○ While there's a growing trend favoring EEG gadgets and brain-computer interfaces, those should not be considered proper clinical neurofeedback devices since they lack individualization and appropriate EEG measurements.

   ○ The neurofeedback software games that provide visual and audio reward have been growing in sophistication and complexity. However, we must reassert that, since neurofeedback is essentially operant and classical conditioning, the games and reward need to remain in a simplified form.

❖ Real-time fMRI (rtfMRI) neurofeedback uses blood-oxygen-level-dependent (BOLD) imaging to measure brain activity by using a magnetic resonance scanner in real time. Its main benefit comes from its ability to target a specific region of interest in the whole brain.

❖ Neurofeedback isn't mainstream because:

   ○ The mainstream line of defense against illness is to write prescriptions or do surgery, which enables mass production. Neurofeedback or rehabilitation/preventive medicine requires effort and time in the beginning, which makes it difficult to mass produce, thus putting it in the background.

   ○ While neurofeedback is people dependent and requires repeated sessions and does seem expensive at the outset, it is actually cheaper over the long term because it makes you better in the future instead of remaining dependent on medication or the system.

- ◦ This is a problem of long-term benefit versus short-term result, and it needs to be addressed. We need to raise people to believe that effort in the beginning is worth ease in the future, and that the way we teach and create change affects the choices people make later.

- ◦ The field doesn't have the lobbyists or the support from insurance companies.

❖ EEG neurofeedback can become your added value: it is a tool that provides change in a fast and easy way, in a happy and comfortable environment.

PART III

A CLINICIAN'S PATH

Supporting someone in their healing requires the right skills and the right tools. But most importantly, it requires a genuine belief and understanding in the process of healing.

Part III is the story of my path to becoming a neurofeedback clinician. I will share the best practices I've learned along the way. Together we'll explore the art of becoming an intuitive behaviorist. We will also explore important learnings in the practice of neurofeedback under Lynette's guidance.

CHAPTER 12

Creating Change

After I'd gained my MSc in neuroimaging, Tarek and I moved to Beirut, Lebanon, to build our lives together. This was in the fall of 2017, before Lebanon's October revolution of 2019 and the horrific explosions of August 4, 2020, a time when our beloved country was still blooming, albeit on the verge of collapse. I was warmly welcomed by Step Together in my new role as a neurofeedback therapist for their students and several other potential in-home clients. My work in Lebanon would be supervised by Lynette and the school's director, Dr. Reem Mouawad.

It was the first time I had properly settled down in a city and was looking forward to being seriously committed to clients in the long term. Up until then, I kept having to leave my clients because I was always moving, and it was so hard to do, especially since I grew to love them. I felt grateful that I could finally support a potential client in the long run.

Meeting the students at Step Together was an exciting process for me. My first step was to observe the students at school and get my first opinion on them. In each classroom I entered, I tried to understand their behaviors. But it never ceased to amaze me how the children unfolded in front of me, how curious they always were of the people around them, and how friendly and loving they were to each other and to themselves.

I also had to meet with all the children's parents to get a

comprehensive assessment and lay out our goals. I asked my questions following Lynette's assessment process in a friendly manner and made sure they shared any concerns they had about neurofeedback. Sitting in front of them, I never failed to remember my mom and how she had once been in their position. I made sure I showed them the understanding and compassion that all parents need and deserve, as my mom once did. Every single parent I met shared the same concerns: they were convinced that it would be impossible to get their child to wear the electrodes, let alone sit with neurofeedback for thirty minutes, and they worried that the session wouldn't be beneficial because of their child's lack of focus.

Gaining Cooperation and Building Trust

Getting the children to sit down for a session is a concern for therapists and parents alike. Especially for children with autism who have hypersensitivity, it is always a challenge. It requires patience, thinking outside of the box, playing, and trusting it will happen. The challenge of getting the child to sit down goes away after a few sessions because generally the child:

1. Will like how neurofeedback makes him/her feel; and

2. Will like the therapist due to the patience and trust they've shown.

However, for the first session, we should follow the child in their play and aim to build trust. While this might take longer than being assertive and asking them to behave, gaining the child's trust is more beneficial in the long term. In fact, asking a child to calm down, to not move their leg, or to stop singing or stop stimming... would be changing their arousal levels. Asking the child to hold it all in means they are unlikely to last the thirty minutes and may be resistant to doing another session ever again. We should aim to get them into a compliant and flexible arousal state before starting our session.

Some ways to build trust:

- ❖ Find the child's motivator. Know what the child likes and use it to be in his/her loop. Love what he/she loves.

- ❖ Gain the child's trust by letting him/her control me at times to make him/her WANT to do neurofeedback rather than feel obliged.

- ❖ Get the child's cooperation through play. Play with the child to show that I am fun and interesting.

- ❖ Process out loud everything that is happening around us to avoid misunderstandings.

- ❖ Always finish on a positive and successful note.

- ❖ Have firm but loving energy.

As much as possible, we should avoid inducing a state of nervousness in the child—even if the intention is to get the best possible effect. Clinical results have shown, again and again, that a perfect connection impedance is not necessary for the session to be effective. Granted, a perfect connection is ideal, but it is better to have a happy child doing neurofeedback with a poor connection than a nervous child doing neurofeedback with a perfect connection.

Their lack of focus shouldn't be a worry either. The child doesn't need to care about how well he/she is doing in the game or even cognitively care about the beeps themselves for the session to be effective. The child attends to whether or not the beeps come in a continuous and smooth sound. The brain's inner need to control those beeps is all that is necessary to make the reward powerful enough for neurofeedback to have its effect.

Finally, it is important to create enough reward for the child to care about doing neurofeedback. We should talk to the child and explicitly say how neurofeedback will help with the main issue the child is having. Even if the child is nonverbal or lacks comprehension skills, we take the time to explain her intention and make it clear that we are here to make the child smart and happy. It is helpful to associate neurofeedback with another reward that the child will be motivated by, such as an activity that the child will be rewarded with later.

To summarize, if you show the children respect and friendship, play with them to gain cooperation and trust, explicitly explain how neurofeedback could help them, and let them be comfortable throughout the process, the children will do as many sessions as needed with comfort, fun, and love.

The parents were eager to start what they saw as an innovative treatment that their child could do in the comfort of the school. I was touched to see how parents in Lebanon were so hungry for change and innovation for their children. The Lebanese government gave no support to children with special needs, which left the parents relentless in their pursuit of improvement.

Following Lynette's assessment process, I went through each student's case under her supervision, and protocols were assigned accordingly.

An Overview of Dr. Louise's Assessment Process

The assessment process starts with setting up the objectives of our assessment. We are ultimately trying to determine the person's overall operating system. The first step to tackling this is to determine if someone needs to raise or lower their arousal state. Thus, we need to understand what the client is seeking and how he is already seeking it. We are aiming to factor into our assessment who the person is, what they like, and how they are enjoying the change. We should use the symptoms and goals as deciders and have the EEG either confirm or deny the supporting statement.

The details are found with observations and questions. If the client is verbal, questions begin the process. If the child is nonverbal, we begin by introducing neurofeedback and play, and we look into the child's behavior for answers. Ask questions or observe to get a sense of his/ her internal experience and add what you see in the client's EEG to inform your answers.

Step 1: Check their medical history.

We first inquire about the client's medical and brain health. We check for a history of brain injury, concussions, seizures, etc. If the person has had a history of any of the above, then we will be cautious in our protocol setup and very closely watch for change and symptoms.

Step 2: Look for their self-medication or compensatory habits.

To get a sense of the client's operating system and internal experience, we examine their self-medication and compensatory habits through categories of questions. We should inquire about their goals, diagnosis, medication, sleeping habits, moods, energy levels, clarity levels, stimulating habits, calming habits, any physical symptoms, strengths, and weaknesses (more details in Appendix I). We aim to determine the core problem as well as the person's preferred way of being. We look for our answers in the details and unfolding of our client.

Step 3: Observe and correlate their physical and psychological state with their EEG waveform and ratios.

When doing a session, we always need to be observant of the client. We first ask them to take a baseline of how they are feeling before starting the session, so as to properly measure any changes. We check for changes in their physical presentation (muscle tone, body temperature, pupil dilation, jaw, shoulders, face color) and inquire about changes in their psychological state during and after the session. Are they feeling different in any way?

While we observe their physiological and psychological changes, we also observe the EEG screen. The most important aspect to keep track of is the ratio between the selected frequency bands, and not so much the numbers in isolation. It's the difference between the numbers that matters because that's where the change happens. We are working on the relationship between the reward and inhibit bands. The distance between them should change over time, but it takes repetition.

Step 4: Let the neurofeedback sessions give us the true answer to their arousal levels.

The questions are just a start, and the information about the person now includes the therapy and the brain's response to the neurofeedback. The real answer regarding their arousal levels comes from both the EEG and the response to the sessions, and we should let the changes from neurofeedback give us more knowledge about which way we should be shifting the brain. As the person is unfolding, you learn more and see the changes happening, whether that person is going in the right direction or not. The therapist and the client work as a team, and together we discover the truth about their arousal state.

The therapy was meant to be done twice a week for sessions of thirty minutes each. Of course, with all of the children, I applied Lynette's principles to get their cooperation. And with each child, it felt like I was sitting with my brother. Not that they had the same symptoms or behaviors as him, but their overall attitude reminded me of his uniqueness. I had learned to accept, understand, and love my brother for who he was, and this attitude extended to all children. I was grateful that I could connect with all these special souls.

Doing neurofeedback following Lynette's approach was categorically different than my previous experience. While I was accustomed to strict rules and control, Lynette was offering a friendlier and more relaxed way, and the results were already showing.

I followed Lynette's practice over the next two years, continually assessing the children, adjusting the neurofeedback protocols, and addressing my clients' behaviors and environments. With her supervision, beautiful changes were happening:

- ✓ H is now able to drink from a cup and bottle when he only used to be able to drink from a straw. He is calmer and expresses himself with more words.

- ✓ S has better and faster communication skills, nags less, and doesn't give up on homework. He can now button his jacket (which he had never done before), he is better at running, and his posture has improved. He can now write and read with more ease.

- ✓ C is now less afraid of people and newness, asks more questions, and is happier.

- ✓ M is experiencing more with her body movements, shares more details, has more awareness, and experiences better sleep patterns.

- ✓ N blocks his ears less often, sits through church, and is more interactive with his family. He performed in the school's end-of-the-year dance show with ease.

- ✓ M is now able to sleep alone in his room at correct times, is less hyper and more descriptive with his words.

- ✓ R is better at walking and has more balance, coordination, and cognition.

- ✓ T is no longer suicidal.

- ✓ Y drools less, talks more, and completes puzzles he couldn't do before.

- ✓ M is now more productive in her work and feels less overwhelmed.

- ✓ … and many more.

Thanks to Lynette's guidance, we created change in my clients, and I felt empowered by the results.

TAKEAWAYS

- ❖ Always aim to build trust and remain fun and interesting to the child to get them to sit down by:
  - ◦ finding their motivator and loving what they love.
  - ◦ letting them control you at times.
  - ◦ gaining cooperation through play.
- ❖ We shouldn't introduce a state of nervousness in the child. Thus we don't ask the child to behave, because:
  - ◦ it will be difficult and uncomfortable for the child.
  - ◦ it could mean that this will make the child resist doing another session.
  - ◦ it would be changing their behavior, thus their arousal levels and brain activity.
- ❖ A perfect connection impedance is preferable but not necessary for the session to be effective.
- ❖ A child doesn't need to cognitively care about the beeps because the brain's inner need for control along with the child attending to whether or not the beeps come in a continuous and smooth sound is sufficient to make the reward powerful enough for neurofeedback to have its effect.
- ❖ Create enough reward for the child to care about doing neurofeedback by:
  - ◦ explicitly saying how neurofeedback will help with his/her main issue.
  - ◦ associating neurofeedback with another motivating reward.

❖ Lynette's assessment process:

○ Simplify the picture and set up the objectives for the assessment. Ultimately, we are trying to determine the person's overall operating system.

○ Try to determine if someone needs to raise or lower their arousal state. Do we want to calm them or brighten them, or both? The symptoms and goals are the deciders of our prognosis.

○ The four steps to assess:

1. Check their medical history.

2. Look for their self-medication or compensatory habits.

3. Observe and correlate their physical and psychological state with their EEG waveform and ratios.

4. Let the neurofeedback sessions give us the true answer to their arousal levels.

CHAPTER 13

Becoming a Clinician

The changes I was witnessing in my clients left me overjoyed. Those successes made me want to work harder and furthered my belief in the power of this tool. Up until now, I had worked hard to better understand the principles behind neurofeedback therapy and tried to determine the best way to practice. However, working with my clients made me realize the importance of being a good clinician as a whole—not just a good neurofeedback clinician. Neurofeedback offered my clients a nonjudgmental and efficient way of dealing with their issues, and this door opened up my relationship with them as their clinician. I was touched by the beautiful relationships I was creating with my clients or their parents.

My experience got even better when I realized how much I was learning from my clients. My heart was full. My work began with healing their brains, but it also involved listening to them and watching them blossom. I learned from each one; they inspired me. I saw fighters. I saw love. I saw devoted parents. I am forever grateful that my clients gave me the honor of being part of their journey.

I hope that as a reader, you understand what that meant for me. Since I was a client of neurofeedback myself and Milo's sister, I felt strongly about my clients and always aimed to understand their circumstances. Being able to give them what Lynette gave to my family was the most beautiful gift. Healing had come full circle.

Under Lynette's supervision, I learned many lessons about how to be a better clinician, which all contributed to helping my clients heal with neurofeedback.

As a clinician, I needed to feel that there was a solution at every turn, and with Lynette's approach, there always was. But most importantly, I understood that the Lynette effect really meant building a friendship with the client and their family, and that rested upon respect, understanding, empathy, and a holistic approach.

The lessons I share below have helped me to transition from a client to a clinician, all while keeping the client perspective in mind.

Empower Your Clients

Throughout the whole process of doing neurofeedback, the work should always be centered on empowering the client we are working with—ensuring that he/she has the power to control their situation. This applies to both the client and their caregiver. If they are empowered, then the choices that follow will be in their best interest and they will feel hopeful. Confidence is built through repeated successes, so aim to empower them by giving them opportunities to succeed as often as possible.

But most importantly, strive to give your client a voice and a say in what life he/she wants to lead. Even if their empowerment doesn't align with what you would advise, work around their reality and toward their goals. It is always better to create change in an empowering way rather than in a resistant manner.

Keep Your Eye on the Goal

In the process of creating change, whether using neurofeedback or another methodology, the path can be bumpy. Long-term change is never linear. Remembering that there will always be ups and downs is empowering in itself. Thus, it's important that we all, clinicians and caregivers alike, keep our eye on the main objective. Little hiccups are bound to happen because humans are volatile, and it is always difficult to point out the cause. In any case, letting small bumps get in the way of our empowerment, of our goal, can be discouraging to all parties. If the client, caregiver, and therapist are all on the same page about what we are trying to accomplish and don't get derailed or start pointing fingers when things go wrong, then we will reach our goal sooner, feeling happy and at peace about the process.

This means that the most important goal for the client must be laid out, said aloud, and constantly reinforced. Determining that goal is often the hardest part and varies over time.

For example, if a child is still expressing some stims but is on his/her way to independence, then we shouldn't let those stims blind us from his/her goal. Working toward a goal in a loving and nonjudgmental way is empowering in and of itself.

When I think of keeping my eye on the goal, I remember the strongly dedicated mothers who never let one derailment get to them. Always looking at the big picture and looking at the next goal enabled them to create more change just by using their energy and time better.

Teamwork

Good things come from effective teamwork. Especially with Lynette's approach to neurofeedback, it is crucial to have all parties as involved as possible. Long-lasting change doesn't happen without teamwork. This means that parents speak with the clinician regularly and understand how the healing process works. While understanding the healing process comes from going through it yourself, it is crucial to realize the importance of teamwork in it.

Understanding the client is also key to reaching the goal. Therefore, ongoing communication and trust are needed. Share your concerns, worries, hopes, and dreams. Share your observations about the child or about yourself. Teamwork means not giving up when things get difficult. Remember that you have someone next to you with a solution at hand. Teamwork requires knowing when to take a hand and when to give a hand. Teamwork, for the client, means telling your clinician about specific secondary effects that occurred that you weren't comfortable with so she has that knowledge for the next sessions. Teamwork, for the clinician, means trusting the client's word, or at least putting it into perspective, to empower him/her with the next session.

With neurofeedback, we are looking for the right protocol that will make the client more empowered. That will come from good teamwork between the client, parents, and therapist. I try to create a team dynamic with the caregiver; when they see that their ability to contribute is respected, they will want to live up to that.

Help Caregivers and Clients See the Change

Part of our job as clinicians is to help caregivers, parents, and clients see the change that is happening. We start by educating them: 1) that change is possible and they can improve, and 2) how to spot these changes. I ask caregivers/clients to remember how things were before neurofeedback and to compare that with the progress they've made. Most people try to attribute the changes to life circumstances rather than neurofeedback, but it's essential to help them see the effects of the therapy. I tell them to try to start neurofeedback with the mindset that it gets all the blame for unwanted changes and all the credit for desired changes in their child or themselves. By attributing everything to neurofeedback, we don't undermine the process and we can look for patterns in the responses over time.

I share the changes I've noticed and ask if that makes sense to them or if they agree. It is crucial to acknowledge and celebrate improvements along the way so we don't get too focused on the goal. By acknowledging, we are empowering. Sometimes I will point out changes I am seeing and ask if the parent sees the same, because in healing we want improvements to generalize (transferring what was learned in one setting to another setting without explicit instruction) to all aspects of one's life, not just with the therapist.

Finally, part of our job as clinicians is to help caregivers not focus or obsess over one or two symptoms alone. This laser focus will not only stop caregivers from seeing changes that could be happening in other areas, but will also stop them from keeping their eye on the bigger goal. With neurofeedback, for example, it is common to do a session to reduce one specific behavior, but sometimes that session won't show changes in that behavior but will show changes and improvements in other areas such as communication or intelligence. A clinician must teach the caregiver or client to take a step back and look at the person as a whole, not just as a collection of symptoms.

I often have to point out changes in the children to their mothers. When I share the specifics of the changes I see, I explain why I think he/she was helped and ask the mom to watch and see if she agrees. Importantly, I stress that if we can improve his/her functioning once, then we can repeat the process and build his/her skills, so he/she has a better ability to learn.

Give Healing the Time it Needs

Healing takes time, and specific steps are needed for the healing process to reach fulfillment.

I had a client with cerebral palsy (movement disorder caused by damage to the brain or abnormal development) who couldn't walk. A combination of neurofeedback and other therapies helped the little girl with her cognition, communication, and strength. She still wasn't able to walk, but she was slowly getting there. We were teaching her brain better balance, coordination, and motor skills by training all the different areas over her sensory-motor strip (Cz, C3, C4, C5, C6), and occasionally some beta reset for her parietal lobes. However, her loving mom focused heavily on her little girl's body, specifically her left leg and foot, which was the main obstacle to her walking. I explained that if she focused on her left leg too much, it would make her daughter focus on it too much, which wouldn't help her learn how to walk. I said, "Her motor skills and balance need to improve before her left leg does."

Understandably, the mom was in a hurry for her daughter to heal. However, that threatened to create a dynamic of seeing her daughter as "broken," which would cause a defensive and rebellious continuation of the problem. To get her to look at the positives, I pointed out how I saw the healing happening in her daughter. Maybe the girl couldn't get her left leg to work, but she would find other ways to make it work through compensation. Her healing was clearly happening, and there was proof in her steps toward it: the girl saw improvements in her motor system (she got better at drawing), in her balance (she now could go horseback riding and sit straight and strong), and in her motor planning (she constantly tried to get up on her own). Thanks to the mom's perseverance, the little girl's determination, and neurofeedback and other therapies, her healing was happening; we just had to keep going. Today this little girl can take steps forward on her own.

Make Your Client Your Partner

To reach a common goal in the fastest and happiest way, we must make the client a partner in the same goal. Making them your partner means asking them to want to reach that goal. We want to help him/her find motivation and to know why they care about reaching the goal. While neurofeedback will help their brain work better to reach it, it is important to also have a behavior change accompanying brain change. Things come easier when you want them.

Consider the following examples of clients who reached their goal by becoming a partner in it:

A fifteen-year-old boy with myotonic muscular dystrophy (long-term genetic disorder that impairs muscle function) was struggling with intense drooling. My assessment showed that when he zoned out, his drooling got worse, and he tended to put his sleeve in his mouth. We theorized nausea salivation might have been happening, and we would need to address it with neurofeedback. Our protocol included C5–C6 (left and right sensory-motor strip) to give him more mouth awareness, as well as F7 (left frontal), which is closer to Broca's area, to help him with language processing, speech production, and nausea salivation by rewarding a higher frequency.

Along with this, I helped the boy to stop his drooling by giving him positive motivation. I told him, "You look so handsome when you swallow your saliva!" or "When you swallow your saliva, you talk so much better and I can understand you!" With time, the boy's drooling reduced dramatically, his overall posture improved, and he has gotten better socially with improved communication.

A sixteen-year-old boy with autism was struggling with verbal communication. With neurofeedback, we trained at F3, T4, T3, and T3–T4, which enhanced his communication and verbal expression beautifully. At the same time, we needed to find ways to make him understand the power of his words. We listened closely and empowered each of his words by letting him be responsible for his language: we only responded to him when he used his words (no response to gestures or sounds), and if we didn't understand the words he used, we asked him to clarify by offering him possible meanings. As we showed him the power and strength of language, he understood what he could accomplish with it. We did the exact same thing with Milo when we were trying to teach him not to use his hands to hit himself during a tantrum. Lynette made my brother aware of the blood on his hands and how unattractive that was to the pretty ladies. She taught him the power of using his words rather than his tantrums.

Balancing Change and Acceptance

As Milo's sister and a clinician in training, I've always battled with balancing two important forces: wanting to create change while also accepting one's fate. My experience taught me that change is possible, but it also taught me to accept and love unconditionally. There is a fine line where both of these realities coexist. While my family has learned (and is continually learning) how to live this way, transmitting this to other families is a challenge. How do we continually push for change and raise the bar while also being accepting of someone's limitations and circumstances? Lynette offered an answer to that question in her book *Miracles Are Made*. She explained that getting results relies on the congruence between three areas: definitions, expectations, and limitations.

❖ Definitions: It is important to define and specify what "good results" mean for a client or a caregiver, and to share those same definitions and goals with your team. Lynette says in *Miracles Are Made*: "Incongruent definitions create confusion and a kind of lazy attempting."[62] As a clinician, Lynette urges us to "try to be the person that wants for the family what they want for themselves while at the same time still showing them that they can want something else."[63]

❖ Expectations: The choices made by the team working around the client and their family are based on their long- or short-term belief system, which we call expectations. Expectations define one's point of completion of a goal, and low expectations can "lead to a lifelong thwarting of skill acquisition,"[64] Lynette says in *Miracles Are Made*. It is also important to recognize the effects of "expectation disparity" between two environments, where the beliefs and expectations of one's capabilities are higher in one environment (e.g., school) than the other (e.g., home).

❖ Limitations: It is crucial to understand physiological presets and acknowledge nature's limitations. While we have found ways to ask and lead the brain to change, results are "limited both by

---

62 Lynette Louise, *Miracles Are Made*, 190.

63 Lynette Louise, *Miracles Are Made*, 186.

64 Lynette Louise, *Miracles Are Made*, 190.

developmental starting points and speed of processing range," Lynette says in *Miracles Are Made*.[65]

The congruence in our definitions, expectations, and limitations enables us to become comfortable with the challenges facing us, to acknowledge the truths in front of us, and to have the confidence and faith to continually create change. With Milo, we often think of the definitions, expectations, and limitations in terms of his progress, and those help shape his growth. I do the same with my growth, and I try hard to teach this to my clients.

Raising the Bar

Last but not least, the concept of "raising the bar" is, in our eyes, the foundation of all of the above lessons and the successes you can create for yourself. Raising the bar means raising your standards and expectations of what is possible, of wanting, thinking, and dreaming of reaching new heights that you couldn't really imagine for yourself or your loved one before.

It is crucial to surround yourself with a team who will continually push you or your loved one further. We urge you to get out of your comfort zone, take that risk, be brave, and believe in yourself, your loved one, and in the world. You can't imagine your child leaving home? Be brave because it might be what is best for his/her independence and freedom. You're so proud of how far your child has come? Don't settle; keep pushing for more.

I see it in my clients' eyes when I urge them to try something that seems unimaginable … the spark of hope can be detected from far away. It's moments like these when I particularly remember my brother and parents. I've witnessed their fear, I've witnessed them taking the leap, and I've witnessed their pride and joy.

* * *

---

65   Lynette Louise, *Miracles Are Made*, 190.

Those lessons I listed above, the ones I had to learn myself as a clinician, were also lessons that I had to assimilate into my own healing. To this day, these lessons are with me when I'm going through my own experiences of change and growth. My family also had to learn those lessons through the years to enable Milo's growth. And because of these lessons, Milo was able to keep growing to become the person he is today.

Chef Milo

The big question of what was next for Milo loomed over us after his time at Dudley College. We decided to follow his interest in cooking and considered the opportunities. Since his time in the kitchen was so productive, whether at the hotel or at home, Soufiane recommended we put Milo through proper training in a cooking school (Soufiane had a background in hospitality). But to make sure this was something Milo really wanted, he spent one week in a bakery shop in Tunisia testing out all the cake and tart recipes (Soufiane's close friend was the owner and gracefully accepted to host him). Baking and pastry required a different skillset, which made Milo even more focused, calm (all his stims stopped), and motivated. Realizing this could be a potential path, Soufiane and my parents searched for a course and found the best option to be a hospitality school in Tunisia (Soufiane's home). The school agreed to offer private tutoring classes to Milo to teach him the ABCs of baking and pastry so he could obtain a degree.

A year into Milo's experience in Hammamet, a small town in coastal Tunisia, he was looking stronger and prouder than ever. Milo spent four days out of the week at school, learning how to make all types of pastries with his tutor and Soufiane. While they started with the most basic recipes, with time, Milo learned to do the more complicated ones: "Madeleines," pain au chocolat, galette des Rois, mille-feuille, marble cakes, croissants, biscuits, fruit tarts, whipped cream. Making pain au chocolat was his all-time favorite.

The rest of the time, Milo worked (for free at first) in the biggest hotel in town. Milo first started helping out in the pastry kitchen, then continued working in the hotel's restaurant buffet, serving food, grilling fish and meat, and frying doughnuts. But the best experience of all was the pizza station, where he learned how to make pizza from scratch, bake it, and serve it to the hotel clientele. He loved being close to people and having contact with them.

Daily videos of Milo's adventures were sent to us to admire. Milo's growth over the year was beautiful process. He improved dramatically in his baking skillset, he matured in his levels of patience, focus, and understanding, and he got better at behaving socially with others. He talked about his experience with pride and worked with a genuine smile on his face (most of the time). His first year was a time for learning and adaptation; he worked tremendously, and his adventures were, at times, hilarious to watch.

Seeing his potential, Mom and Dad wanted to raise the bar even higher for Milo. They wanted him to be more independent, to be able to fail and learn from his mistakes, like all of us. They still do. On Milo's first day, his tutor said it would be impossible for Milo to learn. But Milo impressed us all, and he would keep on blossoming, just as he always has.

It is worth noting that when Milo isn't working, he repeatedly and restlessly inquires about our future trips, future house purchases, or future activities. But we understand that this is his way of communicating with us and of relieving certain anxieties. Milo sometimes hums, screams, and taps his face, but all in a gentle manner. Milo still likes to keep things in order around the house, but without him, the house would be a mess. For so long we prayed for Milo to talk and engage with people, and now he is the biggest blabber we know.

The lessons I learned as a clinician shaped my understanding of healing and, consequently, of Milo's healing. Today, my family and I understand that keeping our eye on his goal toward independence and happiness is more important than aimlessly trying to stop certain behaviors that bother us. We realize that we all have our anxieties in life and that Milo's are just manifested more clearly and explicitly than ours. We let go of his flaws, the same way we let go of each other's flaws. We live with him and enjoy our time with him, all in harmony and in compassion.

We will keep raising the bar for each other, and hopefully, I can spread those lessons back to others.

TAKEAWAYS

❖ Empower your clients. Ensure that they feel in control of their situation. They must feel like the choices are in their best interest, like they have a voice and a say in the life they want to lead. Create change in an empowering manner.

❖ Keep your eye on the goal. Hiccups are bound to happen because humans are volatile, so it is crucial to look at the big picture and to keep working toward the determined goal.

❖ Teamwork: to get to our goal, ongoing communication and trust are key.

❖ Help caregivers and clients see the change. Teach clients to believe that change is possible and to spot and celebrate their successes.

❖ Healing takes time, and specific steps are needed for the healing process to reach fulfillment.

❖ Make your client your partner. We want to help our clients find motivation and reasons to care about reaching their goal. Things come easier when you want them.

❖ Balance change and acceptance. The congruence in our definitions, expectations, and limitations enables us to become comfortable with the challenges facing us, to acknowledge the truths in front of us, and to have the confidence and faith to continually create change.

❖ Raise your standards and expectations of what is possible; want, think, and dream of reaching new heights.

CHAPTER 14

Important Learnings from Neurofeedback

Becoming a neurofeedback clinician has been like riding a roller-coaster. The ups are so thrilling, motivating, and rewarding that I can't imagine doing anything else. But during the lows, I find myself on a guilt trip, and I often feel as if I am experiencing my clients' emotions. Those lows are sometimes traumatic, and I tirelessly fight to make them highs again. While I'm not sure whether this sensitivity is due to my experiences with my brother or is a personal character trait, these emotions have pushed me to further my learning in neurofeedback and in healing.

Several things have helped me cope with those emotions. Consistent self-learning on various topics related to the brain or counseling empowered me with the knowledge that eventually calmed me during those lows. My faith in God was also important. It grew to be my inner strength, as I needed a constant reminder that fate worked in ways that I couldn't predict and that things are always working out for the best. But most importantly, it was what I learned through my professional experience that ultimately made the lows more understandable and predictable.

By following Lynette's approach, I've learned many important lessons about healing and about how life and neurofeedback come into play. I recount some of these lessons below. These stories illustrate why it's important to take an all-of-life, holistic approach to the client.

Making Sense of the Data with the Full Story

Back in 2014, when I was still living in Paris and Milo was visiting, we spent a lot of time together. One afternoon, Milo and I went for lunch at McDonald's (a favorite) and then for a chocolate muffin at Starbucks (another favorite). We were sitting and enjoying our time when he asked me if he could go to the pharmacy to walk around. Milo loved to try beauty products on the back of his hand. I said he could go for five minutes and come back to me. I decided to let this be a learning opportunity for him, so I stayed behind. When he didn't return after the five-minute mark, I realized that something must have gone wrong. I ran to the pharmacy next door and found Milo on the floor picking up coins, surrounded by three saleswomen, who were yelling at him. I ran to them, explained that he was with me, and asked what had happened. In return, one of the ladies yelled at me, "You should never ever leave this boy alone. He is clearly incapable of doing anything. Who do you think you are leaving him on his own? Are you crazy?"

It wasn't her words that broke my heart but the fact that she was saying them in front of Milo. I insisted on knowing what had happened while helping him pick up his coins from the floor, but all I got were screams, no explanation. One of the ladies finally told me that Milo had opened a bottle of gel hand cleaner and put it back. The lady told him he had to buy it, which he had understood, so he went to the cashier to pay for it with his tiny wallet and coins. All of his coins fell on the floor, and he tried to sum up the amount that he owed. It seemed clear the employees had overreacted. My brother had been cooperative, but they hadn't tried to understand him. After all the work Milo had done on himself, I was shocked that people still saw him this way. I was astonished that people could talk this way about him right to his face, as if he couldn't understand a word they were saying. I tried using the moment to teach him the lesson of not opening bottles. At this point, we were both upset about what had happened. We went on with our day and tried to forget about it.

Lynette happened to be visiting a week later. She was sitting with my mom, telling her what sessions she had done on Milo, and let her know that she noticed that my brother had a high ratio of 4/1 of beta to alpha at T3–T4. I came to sit down to listen more as we all discussed Milo's state. It then occurred to me to tell her about the pharmacy incident. Mom and I had noticed Milo acting differently, but we hadn't made the connection. Lynette believed that the event had affected him more than we thought and asked me how I'd dealt with it. She suggested that while I gave Milo feedback on his behavior, I should have given feedback on the women's behavior too. Milo sat down with us and talked about the incident. Lynette told him that some people are mean and won't always understand him, which is why it is important to have good behavior. She also emphasized how important it is to have the full behavioral story to make sense of the data seen on the EEG. This data could have been misinterpreted in many ways, and it was important to talk about it to address and rectify it.

Sometimes We Just Shouldn't Do a Session

Regardless of the efficacy and duration of our neurofeedback training, we must always consider the client's current state before doing a session, because sometimes a session just isn't needed. Even if our intention is right in wanting to create change, it is also about timing and asking what does the brain need now: feedback from the world or from the session? It is part of our job to follow certain behavioral cues and determine whether a session is needed.

For example, I had one client where the frontal training protocol worked great, until one day when a session revved him up because, before the session, he had been in a traumatizing street accident that he hadn't fully told me about. The session made him even more paranoid and worried. It would have been best to hold off on doing a session, allowing him to process what had happened and share it with me.

Likewise, it is often best to let your client learn from the world instead of doing a session when they are doing particularly great. A child in a good positive state with good mood and no sensory problems, for example, is able to learn from the world better. It is tempting to take this chance to train their brain to be stronger in a specific skill, such as communication or focus. However, by challenging their brain at this moment, we can take away their comfort and ease and thus discourage them from learning from their environment. Being more comfortable in their body and feeling stronger will make them want to try new things and be more flexible. Trying to make their skill better by strengthening a brain area could actually make them less comfortable and thus less open to learning. When we feel good, we learn better.

Consider How They Want to Feel

Under Lynette's supervision, I was taught as a clinician to determine my client's level of arousal *and* how they want to grow, what matters to them, and what they most enjoy feeling. It's about picking a protocol that will represent their beliefs, given their answers to the arousal questions, and that is most likely to change them in the direction that they want to go. I, of course, have to factor in their EEG and protocol choices, but without forgetting what they are seeking.

This reminds me of work I did with a dear friend of mine, a thirty-year-old who dealt with depression and suicidal thoughts for five years. He got lost in the use of stimulant drugs as a way of self-medicating his imbalances and needed something to stop his addictions. While his brain always pushed him toward laziness and complacency, he had an inner fight with himself to change and make himself better again. I assessed him as under-aroused, and he craved energy and clarity. As I had learned that we should mimic what people do to themselves to self-medicate, I mimicked his stimulant drug use with neurofeedback.

I started with Cz at 15–18 Hz with a high frequency to increase his arousal for fifteen minutes, and then I switched to F3 at 15–18 Hz. F3 is a great location to mimic the stimulant effect for executive functioning, decision-making, attention, and dopamine release. As the sessions went on, he was dramatically improving (better mood and energy), but he was also still experiencing forgetfulness, lack of attention, and difficulty sleeping. As I followed his behavior and adapted my protocol to his needs, I ended up training him at F3 19–22 Hz and Fp1 19–22 Hz. After ten sessions, he told his family and friends that he hadn't thought he could ever feel this way again in his life. Neurofeedback gave him the feeling he wanted and gave his brain what he needed, and he was able to slowly get rid of how he had previously felt.

It's important to note that rewarding the brain at 19–22 Hz is not common with clinicians. It is common with Lynette, though, as she stumbled upon that frequency when she was training herself following her behavior and neuroanatomy. In *Miracles Are Made,* Lynette describes the 19–22 Hz discovery: "The benzo bump occurs globally in the brain as an increase in activity in a similar high-range-frequency group. The benzo bump is a curious happening not well understood by science. It appears cortex-wide for a small period as a result of taking any of the anti-anxiety medicines known as benzodiazepines such as Valium. I wondered if I hadn't stumbled on the same 'feel good' I would have gotten from the drug without the drug actually being necessary; certainly, my anxiety had been relieved."[66]

Personally, I also train at F3 and Fp1 rewarding 19–22 Hz, and it's the best feeling of "relaxed productivity" for my brain.

---

66 Lynette Louise, *Miracles Are Made: A Real-Life Guide to Autism*, 156–157.

Commitment to Change

I once had a client who was the most brilliant young man, but he struggled with his thoughts, emotions, and states. He used to be a lucid and clear person until depression hit him hard due to recreational drugs that disturbed his system. His brain reacted strongly, making it hard for him to let go of this depression, which had lasted four years with a few hospitalizations. He had a curious mind and was constantly trying to make himself better, to self-medicate, and had enjoyed playing around with drugs and medications to get the feeling he was seeking. Lynette and I agreed that he may have developed stimulant-induced schizophrenia. When I met him, I was called to help him regulate his mood and suicidal thoughts, and importantly, his addiction to stimulants (methamphetamines).

He immediately grasped the concept of neurofeedback and what it could do; he was interested. He knew exactly what kind of feelings he was after and knew why he was using his stimulants. I explained to him that neurofeedback couldn't mimic that stimulant feeling but could give him a similar feeling in a more balanced manner. We started the sessions at C4 13–16 Hz and F3 16–19 Hz, which he claimed made his body feel like a feather. We then did F3 19–22 Hz and C4 13–16 Hz. This made him feel joyful and gave him a stimulant-like feeling; he started experiencing a full night of restful sleep. We also tried T4 8–11 Hz, which made him feel playful, laugh a lot, and remember the past. He kept sleeping well and he felt awesome. Throughout our time, he talked about future possibilities for his life. After four days of having a session every day, he claimed to have that stimulating feeling, and he stopped craving stimulants, as he had just four days before. Neurofeedback helped him get the mood-brightening effect he was seeking while also calming his internal systems. While I did my best to support him, life happened, and our sessions weren't sustainable; neither was the change because he had different plans for his life.

We must want to change if we want to keep healing. While I did everything I could for this client, his commitment to change wasn't there. As powerful as neurofeedback is, it can't create or build a person into someone they don't want to be—they'll just stop doing the sessions. In this case, the client didn't want to be drug-free.

Brains Need Time to Assimilate

It is crucial to give the client time to recuperate, assimilate, and transition after a neurofeedback session. Whether at school or at home, I always try to stay with the client to monitor how they are feeling. During this transitionary period, it is important not to ask something of them and tire them, which would then backfire on how they're feeling. Assimilation is a normal and natural process that occurs after any activity or experience that gives you feedback. With neurofeedback, the changes are stronger, which is why we emphasize the need for a rest period after the session. For some people, that recuperation could be two hours, while for others it could be the rest of the day.

A five-year-old client of mine was having marvelous success with neurofeedback. While she saw improvements in her sleep, mood, and communication, we also witnessed some emotional breakdown the night or day following the session. After further investigation and trying different protocols—always ending up with the same result—we realized that she wasn't getting her recuperation time. Her family and therapists were always asking things of her, and thus, the little girl didn't get the chance to rest or transition. While we want the client to move forward, it's important to ask ourselves this question: "Is the client recuperating, or can I ask something of them?" When the client is tired, the flow of information is reduced, and the inability to focus can lead to anger, which might explain this child's tantrums. As long as she was able to recuperate the next day, her changes kept coming without the tantrum. This girl was not a non-responder. She just needed time.

Some Brains Are More Sensitive

My clinical experience taught me an important reality: some brains are more sensitive than others. I was surprised to see that with some people, change was very evident; I could see how sensitive and aware they were to the subtle sensory shifts. I had a few clients who were able to pinpoint changes in a neurofeedback session within the first minute. These clients had strong experiences of change, and those same clients were the ones who wanted more and committed to feeling better. Clients who are quickly vulnerable to any shifts in state are also sensitive to the suggestions and behaviors of others in their environment. Learning to deal with this sensitivity made me a better clinician because I had to learn how to be patient and discern the most pressing issue. I had to learn not to chase after every complaint; sometimes, doing less is more. I learned the importance of doing one thing at a time, of letting the cumulative effect of a protocol build up before tweaking it. With sensitive brains, we want to build up the person so they take shape before tackling the bigger problems. We want to find what stabilizes them, because that's what they need.

Use qEEG for Extra Information

While we wouldn't encourage a qEEG to be done, when it is available, it is always considered great extra information that we should use in our assessment and protocol choices. Many of my clients have had a qEEG done, which I've been able to use to either confirm or deny what I am already doing. I appreciate working as a team with other therapists on this.

When I get a qEEG, I look to see if what we are targeting shows up in the qEEG and to evaluate whether the recommendations align with what we are doing already. I look for any indications that a change is required, and I also try to read the qEEG holistically and associate the EEG to my client's behavior. Clients usually ask for a better explanation of their qEEG; they are rarely satisfied with the summary provided. I take the time to explain the frequencies and areas that seem problematic, relate it to the client's behaviors, and show how we are tackling them.

* * *

While I realize that I have only scratched the surface, I am grateful for how these lessons have shaped me. I am expecting many more lessons to come as, at the time of this writing, I am pregnant with a baby boy. I feel blessed and excited to finally be able to understand the journey of motherhood, a journey that I have looked at with admiration throughout all these years with my clients.

TAKEAWAYS

❖ It is important to have the full behavioral story to make sense of the data seen on the EEG so you don't misinterpret it.

❖ Sometimes a session just isn't needed. It is part of our job to follow behavioral cues to determine whether the brain needs feedback from the world or from the session.

❖ Consider how the client wants to feel. Pick a protocol that is most likely to change them in the direction of who they want to be, what matters to them, and what they enjoy feeling the most.

❖ We must want to change, must be committed to change, if we want to keep healing.

❖ Give brains the time to rest, recuperate, and assimilate after a session.

❖ With sensitive brains, we want to find what stabilizes them first because that's what they need.

❖ When a qEEG is available, it is great extra information that we should use in our assessment and protocol choices.

CHAPTER 15

A Practice to Follow

As I grew as a clinician, my experiences helped me bridge the gap and make sense out of my confusion between the research and clinical worlds. I realized it was important to use the best of both worlds and that is exactly what Dr. Louise's methodology was about:

- ❖ On one hand, it is an unfolding approach that requires focus and flexibility (clinical).

- ❖ On the other hand, it relies heavily on using neuroanatomy as a guide, which requires continuous learning (research).

The steps summarized below will show you how you can use neurofeedback more holistically by integrating Dr. Louise's overarching model within your practice however you see fit.

Step 1. Initial Assessment

The first step is to conduct a basic assessment of the client: to gather as much information as possible. To get a better picture of my client, I observe the client's behavior to find clues about his/her physiological functioning and neuroanatomy, rather than relying on a 22-placement cap to analyze the EEG. We use the symptoms and goals as deciders for the training and then have the EEG either confirm or deny the supporting statement. Most importantly, the assessment doesn't stop here; we continually assess while we train the client. The client will unfold at every step and every session, providing us with more information about what they need.

What is his/her operating system?

First, simplify the overall picture by setting up the objective of the assessment. Why did he/she seek help? What does he/she need help with? However, to help the client with his/her objective, we need to determine how the client operates. We aim to become symptom-oriented rather than diagnosis-oriented. We want to read the client's behavior rather than his/her diagnosis or presentation because internal states explain external behaviors. Once we know how the client operates, we can get the right tools to help him/her heal. The symptoms and goals are the deciders of the prognosis.

As we try to determine their operating system, we also try to determine what the client is seeking. Who does the client want to be? What matters to them? What do they enjoy feeling the most? We are looking to understand them enough to be able to pick a neurofeedback protocol that will change them in the direction they want to go.

We use a comfortable, friendly style as we check their feelings and thoughts through questions. We always check with the client, even if it seems like he/she lacks self-awareness of problems or is unable to communicate. We check in order to give him/her power and show respect. If we can't obtain this information from the client, then we ask his/her family, friends, therapists, or teachers. Most importantly, we try our best not to get distracted by diagnostic labels or descriptive labels because the goal is to look through those labels and determine how they operate.

Follow the behavior and use neuroanatomy for guidance

As we try to determine the client's operating system, we follow their behavior to give us more knowledge about him/her. Following behavior means following clues in their emotional, behavioral, and cognitive responses.

We let the behavior speak for itself. We keep following these clues as guidance about their operating system. These behavioral clues are essential since they will give us a window into what's going on in their brain. Then we look for a neuroanatomy fact that will provide an explanation to those behavioral clues. Understanding the brain means understanding what we should attribute a behavior to, which could then point to a possible solution.

Questions begin the process of understanding the client's behavior by opening a window into their internal state. We ask questions to get a sense of their internal experience while coping with whatever brain wave data we may discover. If the client is nonverbal, we begin by introducing play and watching for behavioral clues. We put off questioning the parents until later because it's essential to get pure information that hasn't been filtered by a parent's or teacher's beliefs around their diagnostic label.

For example, when working with the students at school, I observe them during recess or from the window in their class. I watch their behavior and ask myself: What do I see? What does this behavior mean in the brain? When I see my nine-year-old client with a sensory overload constantly close his ears and bite his lips, does it mean he has a dysfunction with his right temporal lobe? When I see my fourteen-year-old client with myotonic muscular dystrophy drool from his mouth, is his drooling due to problems with his mouth sensation over the sensory-motor strip?

Arousal and compensatory lens

As we try to determine the client's operating system by following his/her behavior and using neuroanatomy as our guide, it's important to always keep in mind the arousal and compensatory lens. If the client isn't in balance, then we should probably expect him to have some compensatory actions to achieve homeostasis. We must ask: How does the client self-regulate back to balance? We assess all those behavioral clues through the arousal and compensatory lens. We remember that some arousal states may overlap, and thus try to differentiate between what is high or low arousal. We want to determine if we need to raise his/her arousal state or lower it. Do we want to calm or brighten him/her, or both? We also think of neuroanatomy through the arousal and compensatory lens. Should we brighten the client by working on the left frontal lobe or on the right parietal lobe? The answers are found in the details. We always aim to look at the wholeness of a situation and look at the climb and trajectory of different behaviors.

Thinking in arousal and compensatory terms means taking into consideration the possibility that a parent or client could be misinterpreting a behavior and thus misinforming us. Is an arousal state being mislabeled? When a client tells me he/she is overly anxious, is the anxiety a compensatory mechanism to his/her low state? When the mom of a Down syndrome boy tells me her son is hyper and can't sleep, does that mean he is over- or under-aroused? When my eight-year-old client with autism screams and runs around the school, is the running to calm himself or to get energy?

We put all the elements together to make a story

As we try to determine the client's operating system, we follow his/her behavior, use neuroanatomy as our guide, and filter all the information through the arousal and compensatory lens. We must also apply this thinking to all the elements of the client's life and link them together. It is not right or fair to see a behavior, such as tantrums at school, and directly attribute it to his/her overactive parietal lobe or assume he/she needs his/her arousal lowered, because we still don't have their full story. It is crucial to gather all relevant information about him/her to link all the elements together and find the best possible prognosis. After we've investigated each element, we combine them all to help us understand their operating system and goals.

We inquire about and observe the following elements and then investigate how each element could be contributing to the client's overall state:

1. History/Neuroanatomy/Physiology

   Any information is relevant to the client's health and brain. Check for any medical history. Brain injury? Seizures? Hormonal problems? How was his/her developmental growth? Any brain defect from birth? Lazy eye? Hand tremor?

2. Environment

   Obtain information about his/her environment. Does he go to school? Does the school make him nervous? How is his/her teacher? Does he/she use other therapies? If his/her therapist is calm, how does that contribute to his/her state? Any siblings? How are his/her parents? If his mother is always anxious, how does that affect him/her?

3. Medication/Supplements

   Does the client take any medication or supplements? What has he/she taken in the past? If he/she has taken anything, how did that make him/her feel? Why was it stopped? How did the Ritalin he/she once took contribute to his/her arousal levels? How about the SSRI?

4. Behavior

   Look for behavioral clues that could give insight into the client's overall state. How is his/her sleep? Mood? Energy? Focus? Sensory integration? Strengths and weaknesses at school? How is his/her communication? Do his/her behaviors help him/her to stimulate or calm? How does his/her lack of focus contribute to his/her overall state?

The information gathered should now help determine the client's operating system, needs, and goals.

A protocol to begin with

Once we understand the overall picture, we have to decide on a protocol to start with. The goal is to find the ideal frequency bandwidths to reward and inhibit and the right electrode placement. We either do the opposite of how the client operates, or we strengthen his/her form of self-medication. If they are anxious and keeping busy helps them, we can either train them with neurofeedback to calm down with some temporal lobe training (opposite of how he/she operates) or to have more energy with some frontal lobe training (strengthen his/her form of self-medication). We are aiming to factor in who the client is, what he/she likes, and how he/she is enjoying the change. What feels better?

The prognosis comes either by mimicking what he/she is doing to him/herself and then shaping it toward the goal or by giving him/her the opposite because what he/she is doing is a bother. Neurofeedback gives us a choice. Once we put the electrodes on the client's head, we will have to see if the EEG matches the behavior. If it is too difficult to choose a protocol from the start, we can always start with a Cz placement with either a high-frequency reward (if the client needs to raise his/her arousal) or a low-frequency reward (if the client needs to lower his/her arousal). No matter what protocol we started with, we now have to pay close attention to the changes and follow the client's response to treatment.

Step 2. Observe during the Session

Now that we have started a neurofeedback session, we can observe the client's EEG by watching for behavioral changes and letting the neurofeedback give us more knowledge about which way we should be shifting the brain. We need to be observant and pay attention to the client and the changes, as it is through their EEG and behavioral observation that we'll know if they are heading in the right direction of healing.

Watch for EEG

During the session, we watch for EEG patterns and paroxysmal events, for overfiring and under firing and artifacts. We keep track of the ratios between the selected frequency bands. The objective is to look for patterns and any correlations with the client's behavior.

Watch for behavior

During the session, we also need continuous behavioral feedback from the client because the EEG numbers can't speak on their own. We watch the behavioral presentation and any shifts of state. We watch their expression, color, physical activity, and pupil dilation, and we note any change. Before the session starts, we take a baseline by noticing how he/she is feeling, and then throughout the session, we check in with the client on how he/she is feeling compared to his/her baseline (clarity, energy, calmness, mood…). We ask/notice whether they feel or behave differently in any way. We try not to be too distracted by the subtle shifts of state during a session, as they are usually transient. We only make a note of the apparent changes.

Compare what we see on the screen to the behavior

We ask questions and add what we see in the client's EEG to inform our answers so that we can attempt to understand how the client's brain functions when firing those particular brain waves in that particular area of the brain. Importantly, we compare what we see on screen against what we see in the behavior. Are there correlations? If the assessment of the client showed he/she was under-aroused, then hopefully we will see much more low-frequency brain waves than high-frequency brain waves. We want to check three things all the time: the client's presentation, the client's frequency band ratios, and the client's EEG waveform. We are always waiting for change: the goal is to create and watch for change.

Is the client heading in the right direction?

Throughout the session and after it's over, we ask whether the client is heading in the right direction of healing or not. As the client is unfolding, we learn more about him/her and see if the changes happening are working toward our goal.

Wherever the client is headed at the end of the session, the effect will grow bigger over the next twenty-four hours. It takes time for the brain to assimilate and recuperate, and it depends on each person. In the first thirty minutes after the session, we try not to be too distracted by behaviors as that is the adjustment period. Unless the client is feeling some kind of discomfort, we write down what we notice and wait for them to assimilate. Other than feeling tired (which is common since neurofeedback can be taxing for some), the client should feel good overall (he/she may say it is weird to feel different). The client may need to recuperate, and we should allow them their personal style in this healing process.

Whenever possible, try to stay with the client for thirty minutes after the session so that other people aren't confused by this transitionary period. After about thirty minutes, the direction of the changes should be pretty clear, and that is when we can tell if he/she feels better or worse. If we see anything alarming, take the time to do neurofeedback again and rectify his/her arousal state.

Step 3. Follow the Client's Response to Treatment

It is the neurofeedback sessions that will give us the true answer to the client's arousal levels. The real answer regarding their operating system will come from their response to neurofeedback. Neurofeedback itself is the perfect lens for thinking in arousal and compensatory terms. Neurofeedback provides us with EEG information, and as neurofeedback creates a direct change in the client's arousal levels, we can directly observe whether the client liked that change or not. We need to change the protocol accordingly in the next session based on how the client reacted to the previous session.

Track changes between sessions

Only write down any changes since the previous session. Inquire about changes they noticed and always monitor the client before and after the session. We look for desirable and undesirable changes in all categories: bowels, energy, mood, appetite, focus, pain, body image, sensory issues, fine and gross motor challenges, balance, tics, stutters, problem-solving, habits, communication, certain skills… The focus of this therapy is change. But it's important to note that, because of the brain's interconnectivity, it may take a while to get to the main goal, as other areas need to heal first. Any occurring changes, even if they are not the ones we're after, will help determine how the client operates and thus help us get to the goal. So, we note any changes that have taken place and watch for patterns to emerge. We make sure we keep an eye on what is improving so that if we need to change the protocol, we keep those improvements and correct for problems as they emerge. We gather information and choose the protocols fast enough to keep the client enjoying the therapy.

Adjusting the protocol

As we follow the client's changes in behavior, we use neuroanatomy as our guide and filter all the information through the arousal and compensatory lens. We then factor in the goals and choose the next step in protocol adjustments. We keep thinking about arousal and compensatory terms. If we trained at a too-high frequency group, we look for over-arousal symptoms and reverse them by training at lower frequencies or by shifting the site. If we trained at a too-low frequency group, we look for under-arousal symptoms and reverse them by training at higher frequencies or by shifting sites.

We can adjust the protocol throughout the session or the next time the session is due. For example, if we trained on the left at a high reward and the client feels nervous, then next time we will train on the right at a medium reward. We make changes based on the client's feedback and by observing the client. We can also balance the training time between the left and right hemispheres or adjust the frequencies. We tackle each challenge, one at a time, as the client changes because change is never linear. Once we figure out the correct frequencies and locations, we experience only improvement, alleviating symptom after symptom day upon day, and neurofeedback becomes the gift that keeps on giving.

Keep putting all the elements together to update the story

As we follow the client's response to treatment, we need to consider all the elements of the client's life. As we try to make a story out of all the elements, it will bring clarity and help us determine if the client's life elements are contributing to his/her healing or getting in the way.

Inquire about and observe the following:

1. History/Neuroanatomy/Physiology
2. Environment
3. Medication/Supplements
4. Behavior
5. EEG

   What do we see in the EEG? Any overlap between the EEG and his/her behavior? Are there any patterns? If we see an excess of delta in the left prefrontal lobe, how does that contribute to his/her overall state?

6. <u>Response to treatment</u>

Closely inspect the client's response to the neurofeedback session. Check how his/her behavior has changed and ask whether we were able to change his/her physiological state in the right direction.

Step 4. Positive Behavior and Cooperation

Regardless of how well we understand the client's operating system and find the ideal protocol, it is crucial to ensure that the client has an enjoyable and successful experience with neurofeedback. This means we need to have the right personal and clinical skills to behave appropriately with the client. While this applies to adults, this is especially true and important for children—even more so for clients with special needs. It is by showing the client respect and friendship, playing with him/her to gain their cooperation and trust, explicitly explaining how neurofeedback could help him/her, and letting him/her be comfortable throughout the process that I ensure an enjoyable and successful healing experience.

Sit down with the client, build trust, and follow his/her play

Since we need the client to cooperate in doing a neurofeedback session, we must be willing to try anything to connect and play with the client to get cooperation. We learn to know what the client likes, love what they love, and play enough with him/her to show that we are fun and interesting to him/her. We work to gain the child's trust by letting him/her control us at times to make them WANT to do neurofeedback rather than feeling obliged to.

With my students at school, I always make sure they enter the neurofeedback room feeling all the incredible excitement and happiness I have from being with them. I take time to learn what they like and use it to earn their trust. For them to find neurofeedback attractive, I select images of their interests to show when we're playing the neurofeedback game. The reward beep accompanies a piece of a puzzle on a screen, and that puzzle is of an image of something they love: cars, Looney Tunes, SpongeBob... you name it. They see what they love on the screen. We then talk about those images together or sit silently if they prefer. If I have to sing the Space Jam song "I Believe I Can Fly" at every session to make the student comfortable enough, then I do.

For especially challenged children, I have them watch a video of something they like that keeps them calm and interested. If that's what it takes to make them feel calm enough to do a session, then why not? We know the session is effective regardless of their focus on the game anyway. A great way of earning children's trust is to wear the electrodes myself first and make the game seem fascinating and super fun. For students who are extremely sensory sensitive, getting them to wear the electrodes takes time and patience. I usually start with having one electrode on me while the other is on them to make it seem like we were playing together. If they refuse to feel it on their head, I try to place it away from their scalp, so they won't feel it, but they know it's there. Once they've accepted to have it on, we count seconds together of how long they should keep it on and make a game out of it. Eventually, it increases long enough so we can do a full thirty-minute session.

Finally, I always take time to play with them before or after the session, even if just for five minutes, so they know I am their friend. Through that, I get to teach them what friendship is and use the phrase Lynette swears by: "We play your game (whatever they like), and we play my game (neurofeedback). That's what friends do!"

Don't ask the client to behave

Try as much as possible not to introduce a state of nervousness in the client, even if that means that you get an artifact in the EEG. Don't ask the client to calm down or to stop behaviors that are interfering with the EEG. Understand that those behaviors are part of the client's self-regulation, and thus we need to work with them. It is vital to keep the client in his/her regular state rather than ask him/her to do something that will make him/her uncomfortable. It is better to have a happy client doing neurofeedback with a poor connection than a nervous client doing neurofeedback with perfect connection.

With my students at school, I let them do neurofeedback on my office couch rather than the desk if that makes them more comfortable. If they feel like lying on the couch, then that's fine as well. If they want to stare out the window while doing the session, that's also fine. If a student is scared of the storm outside and wants to close his/her ears and eyes, then that's fine. If he/she wants to talk throughout the session because that makes them feel better, then that's fine.

All of it is fine, as long as the electrodes stay in place, and there isn't too much interference. If I need to stand up with them as I hold the amplifier, then that's fine. If I need to move the amplifier's location because they're lying on the couch, then that's fine. If my connection gets bad for a minute or two because my client needs to close his/her ears because he/she is afraid of the storm, I give them that time to relax, to help him/her through, and it's all fine.

All the children responded despite the fact that they were dancing, wiggling, running, pacing, with their backs to the computer and the amplifier attached to their shirts. They would shift states and get the effect I wanted for them, and they would monitor and control the strength of the feedback with the level of attention they gave the machine. This freedom helped them feel safe, in control, and a partner in their healing.

Explain what neurofeedback will help them with

While we understand that the client doesn't need to care about the beeps or the game for the session to be effective, it's also important to create enough reward for the client to care about doing neurofeedback. Whether you're working with a child or an adult, with special needs or not, always take the time to explain how neurofeedback can help their main concern in a friendly and interesting manner. I also like to associate neurofeedback with another reward that my client would get after the session and thus be motivated by.

With every student or client, I always determine the thing that bothers them the most, and then tell them how neurofeedback will help them. I tell my client with cerebral palsy that neurofeedback will help her walk, my other client that it will help him be happy. I tell my client with autism that neurofeedback will help him not hurt himself, my other client that we will help him talk and ask for what he wants. I try to make neurofeedback look beneficial to them, in their own words. Whether young or old, challenged or not, we all have an awareness of ourselves; we all want to feel strong and happy. I make sure they understand that neurofeedback will help them become who they want to become.

Step 5. Behavioral Teaching and Addressing the Environment

Throughout our process of neurofeedback, always remember the feedback that the client's environment is providing him/her. Realize that doing neurofeedback alone is not enough and that other forms of feedback are equally important. If the client's brain is changing, then his/her environment needs to follow accordingly.

Add teaching to a behavior

I am generally asked to address and fix a behavioral issue with neurofeedback. While I could have the best neurofeedback protocol targeted for that issue, it probably still won't be enough to reach the goal of properly addressing the behavioral concern. Behavioral teaching always needs to accompany healing; it can make all the difference. Behavioral teaching means making the client aware of the presence of the behavior, showing them the consequences of that behavior, and giving them a reason to address that behavior. Finding a reason the client cares about enough to want to address that behavior is what will make all the difference. People are used to hearing about how bad that behavior is, especially children, rather than what is good about addressing that behavior. We want to make the client a partner in the goal.

I had two students who struggled with drooling. To tackle drooling, for example, we can use a neurofeedback protocol that addresses the mouth through c5–c6 at 14–17 Hz to get them to use their sensory system and muscles properly. But that wouldn't be enough, so I also talked about their drooling and showed them in the mirror to make them more aware of it. I explicitly told them that neurofeedback would help reduce the drooling. Importantly, though, I gave the children a reason to care about wanting to stop the drooling so they would be motivated to stop.

Address the environment

Considering the client's environment is essential to providing meaningful treatment. Neurofeedback increases the speed of healing and supports the feedback the client is getting from his/her environment; therefore, we want to ensure that the feedback of the environment the client lives in coincides with the changes we are creating in his brain and him/herself with neurofeedback. We can address the environment by speaking to the client's family, caregivers, friends, or teachers and letting them know what we are working toward.

To clarify, once the client begins to function differently, the world he/she lives in will give different feedback. He/she will hear from the environment how better he/she is at talking, understanding, and writing. He/she will hear about how much happier, calmer, or productive he/she seems. The more this is said to the client, the more they will begin to believe it, and what they believe they are, they will become. Yes, positive reinforcement is crucial because people's opinions and perceptions are feedback, and that feedback results in behaviors and emotions that can be positive or negative to someone's healing. Therefore, the client's environment needs to be rewarding him/her in all the right places. Without this piece, we will end up with unpredictable changes. We want to plant positive and realistic messages to create a better environment for the child to grow.

Case Studies Using Dr. Louise's Five-Step Process

The following case studies are from my personal experience and illustrate how I follow Lynette's approach.

Six-year-old girl

History/Neuroanatomy/Physiology: First met this client as a five-year-old girl with cerebral palsy. She had had several general tonic-clonic seizures. MRI results showed possible damage in the sub-cortical white matter of the parietal lobes as well as possible damage in the left frontal subcortical white matter.

Environment: Wonderful parents and two older siblings. She went to a school for special needs and was in a class with supportive students whom she looked up to. Her mother was very understanding and supportive of her daughter. The girl did many other therapies.

Medication/supplements: Takes Keppra (levetiracetam) to treat her epilepsy.

Behavior: She struggled with gross and fine motor skills, with auditory and visual memory, and with poor balance and body coordination. She had a short concentration span and struggled with word retrieval and sentence structure. Her energy fluctuated between low to hyperactive. She woke up at night several times and generally woke up earlier than she should. The girl's mood could switch quickly from being happy to angry. Behavioral observation showed that she loved to play with games and challenged herself to do activities that were difficult for her. She liked to open doors and liked to walk and run without necessarily holding hands for support. She liked to keep busy with her hands. She was about to begin potty training.

Assessment story: With cerebral palsy, we want to work on getting the brain and body more connected. Her assessment showed that she was probably looking for external stimulation to brighten herself up and give her focus. While her and her mother's commitment and motivation to improve would help her, we had to take into account her seizure disorder with neurofeedback. Her medication was probably making her feel low and tired, and we needed to keep an eye on whether her other therapies were overtiring her. We needed a protocol that would help with her motor skills, balance, coordination, memory, and verbal communication.

A protocol to start with: Training at Cz is generally a good place to start with cerebral palsy. Cz is in the center of the sensory-motor strip and works on the somatosensory cortex for sensory-motor integration, mental flexibility, and attention, and is also connected to the hypothalamus. With seizure disorders, Lynette taught me to always inhibit all frequency brain waves, including the reward band, to discourage spiking amplitudes of even the desired brain waves. We want to do our best to avoid any paroxysmal activity and seizures: Cz rewarding 12–15 Hz and inhibiting 0–4, 4–15, 15–36 Hz.

Response to treatment: After 20 sessions of Cz rewarding 12–15 Hz and inhibiting 0–4, 4–15, 15–36 Hz, the girl shows improvements in clarity of thought, is sharing more details, has longer communication periods, and is more assertive. She generally has more energy, better sleep, and better attention. She seems to be experiencing more with her body. She has more awareness of her questions. She no longer needs a support person standing next to her at all times. But the mom wants to add emphasis on her vocabulary. It seems like she wants to talk but can't find the words. She has issues with potty training, as she doesn't realize when she needs to go and so is not able to feel or control it.

Over time her response to treatment had to take many factors of her life's element into consideration. When the girl had a seizure, we had to adapt our protocol. When the girl had a change in medication, we had to adapt our protocol. When her environment changed regarding her potty training and sleep, we had to adapt our protocol.

Nine-year-old boy

History/Neuroanatomy/Physiology: A nine-year-old boy with learning disabilities. No relevant medical history. Varying doctors had given him different diagnoses: ADHD, ADD, DCD (developmental coordination disorder), or mild to moderate autism, but the label was unclear (and not necessary). He had poor motor skills, a speech deficit, and maybe was dyslexic.

Environment: He had great supporting parents and one sister. Father lived in a different country due to work and only saw his son once every two months. Parents were focused on academics. The boy went to a school for special needs and was in a classroom with nine other students with special needs, with two teachers supervising them. He also worked with a speech therapist who put a lot of emphasis on the boy's lack of skills in reading and writing.

Medication/supplements: No medication or supplements were ever taken.

Behavior: The boy was verbal but struggled with sentence structure. He had difficulty with math and putting meaning to numbers. He wrote poorly and struggled with reading. It was difficult for him to sustain his attention, especially with his academic work. He struggled with physical activity, especially using his fingers, walking, and running. He generally cycled through phases of having great energy to poor energy. His sleep patterns were good. His mood wasn't affected; he was generally happy, but he could get angry and snappy, rather than sad, when things didn't go his way. He was shy and had difficulty interacting and making friends but was very talkative about his interests.

Assessment story: The boy's inability to self-regulate is shown in how his energy cycled. He was probably giving into his state when he had no energy and fighting his state when he had too much energy. Physical activity and motor skills were difficult for him, which could have meant that he needed to increase his arousal state to help him go on with everyday life. The boy's difficulties with reading and writing were probably due to problems in his brain's auditory and language areas.

His lack of focus was also a sign that he needed his arousal increased, as it was contributing to his academic and physical difficulties. It is possible that the boy felt distracted in the classroom at school and was also nervous because of the other students. His parents' strong focus on academics, which was being fed by the speech therapist, could have also contributed to making him less motivated to learn. It is also possible that his difficulties in reading and writing and in socializing came from a lack of confidence in himself.

NF: Our goal with neurofeedback was to make him feel clearer and brighter, and to make him more available and capable of learning. We wanted to help him feel good in his mind and body so that he could focus and learn. We used bipolar placements to work on his brain pathways and work on different areas in his brain to help with his objectives holistically.

Dyslexia: Strengthened the pathways between his left and right parietal lobes (P5–P6), rewarding 12–15 Hz for ten minutes (mid-frequency reward to not lower his arousal).

Language and communication skills: Strengthened the pathways between his Wernicke and Broca's areas (P5–F7), rewarding 14–17 Hz for ten minutes with a mid-frequency reward for brightening his left hemisphere.

Possible auditory dyslexia: Improved integration between auditory, visual, perceptual, and memory inputs by strengthening the pathways between his left and right temporal lobes (T3–T4), rewarding

12–15 Hz for ten minutes (mid-frequency reward, as we don't want to calm him too much).

Motor planning, speech, working memory: Focused by brightening his left frontal lobe (F3), rewarding 15–18 Hz for ten minutes (mid- to high-frequency reward to brighten him).

Address the environment: While neurofeedback helped him with his brain, we also needed to address the environment. As the boy changed and felt better in his brain and body, he would be more capable of learning, but that didn't mean that the parents should focus even more on his academic skills. With special needs, we focus on what the child needs to know. We should teach academic skills in what they like by making it fun. We need to try to get the child to want what we want. It was important for this boy to be happy because when he was happy, he gained confidence, and through that, he would enjoy more successes. I explained to the mom how any child is capable of anything when he/she is feeling happy and comfortable. When he felt good, that was when she would get cooperation.

Response to treatment: With the cumulative effect of this protocol, neurofeedback helped him improve his spelling and reading. He has developed more awareness of himself and his surroundings. He is now more talkative and interactive with people. He elaborates and gives more details in his sentences. His vocabulary when he talks has become more sophisticated, and he is able to find his words. He replies with logic. He has become calmer and has better focus. He is more cooperative and complains less. Doing homework has become easier, and he is now more patient. He can now tie his shoes all by himself, which he couldn't before, is independent, and now does tae kwon do as an extracurricular activity.

TAKEAWAYS

1. Initial Assessment
   - ❖ What is his/her operating system?
   - ❖ Follow behavior and use neuroanatomy as guidance
   - ❖ Arousal and compensatory lens
   - ❖ We put all the elements together to make a story
   - ❖ A protocol to begin with

2. Observe during the session
   - ❖ Watch for EEG
   - ❖ Watch for behavior
   - ❖ Lay what we see on the screen against the behavior
   - ❖ Is the client heading in the right direction?

3. Follow the client's response to treatment
   - ❖ Track changes between sessions
   - ❖ Adjust the protocol accordingly through the arousal and compensatory lens, follow behavior and use neuroanatomy as guidance
   - ❖ Keep putting all the elements together to update the story

4. Positive behavior and cooperation
   - ❖ To get the client to sit down, build trust and follow his/her play
   - ❖ Don't ask the client to behave
   - ❖ Explain what neurofeedback will help him/her with

5. Behavioral teaching and addressing the environment
   - ❖ Add teaching to a behavior
   - ❖ Address the environment

Conclusion

I n chapter 1, I described what happened when we visited a mosque in Damascus, Syria. Almost fifteen years later, we were all back in another mosque. This time, we were visiting the Sheikh Zayed Mosque in Abu Dhabi, the largest mosque in the UAE, designed by a Syrian architect. It has become an important place of worship while also serving as a landmark to unite Islamic cultural diversity with art and architecture.

It was peak season during Christmas break, and entering the crowded mosque was stressful for us all. However, the mosque looked like Aladdin's Agrabah from Disney, which immediately made us feel like we were in a fantasy world. My family, along with my husband and other relatives, walked around the huge mosque and took in its beauty and splendor. While we all wandered in different directions, my husband, my two brothers, and I continued on our own and ended up outside, waiting for the rest of the family to join us. I was still admiring the mosque's minarets and domes when I turned around to find Milo laughing and talking to my husband with a big smile on his face. And just as I was staring at him, a thought hit me: *the last time we were all together in a mosque, Milo had one of the biggest and most traumatic meltdowns in his life.* And today, here he was, despite the even more overwhelming and stressful environment, happily standing with ease and enjoying every minute of it. I whispered this thought to my youngest brother, and we took a mental picture of the moment, knowing how perfectly this occasion captured Milo's journey. Ironically, it was me who ended up having a meltdown that day, not Milo.

We gave Milo the tools to let him grow and be who he wanted to be. We gave him options and choices as he grew into adulthood and helped him find the voice that he yearned to use. Milo still isms with his humming, running, and repetitive talk, but none of these get in the way of his life, or our lives. Milo has learned to express his concerns, to ask for time, and to lean on the tools that help him process the world. Today my brother looks more like a "cute weirdo" than someone who has autism. We don't expect Milo to ever become "normal" (what is normal, anyway?), and we are genuinely happy with where he is and who he is.

We are often asked if Milo truly enjoys his work. While we will never be able to confidently know the answer, we do know Milo is on the right track to learning a trade that is appropriate to his skillset and will help him receive an income and independence. We also realize his confidence and happiness stem from the repeated successes that his work provides. He seems happy, calm, and at ease when he's working. My dad says the best thing is that Milo has continually improved and he is still improving to this day, which makes us hopeful that anything can happen—there is still space for change. This is something my mother values, as she always reminds us of the importance of keeping things flexible for Milo and allowing him to try whatever comes his way, rather than putting him in a box and limiting him. What we know for certain is that, as long as Milo is happy, he will be able to figure things out. We trust him, and we trust that all of us together will work toward the right thing for him.

Embracing neurofeedback and the understanding that we can't fix others but we can change ourselves has made a lot of difference to my family and our relationships. We have learned to understand behavior, not to pass judgment, to adapt to the people around us, and to continually improve ourselves. Milo asks for neurofeedback when he needs it, and so do I. Knowing we can reach out to neurofeedback whenever we need it has brought us power, comfort, and patience.

Having the ability to help family and friends on the spot whenever in need, the ability to offer an alternative, a choice for them to decide who they want to be, is what I am most grateful for.

Using neurofeedback to change yourself means creating a new path. And I believe this is exactly what happened to my siblings and me. The four of us did neurofeedback from a fairly young age, our brains changed, and we charted new courses. Who knows what would have happened if we hadn't had that tool? Taking care of yourself should be natural and essential; it should be a prerequisite to taking care of your loved ones.

All this was possible thanks to Lynette and her approach to neurofeedback—which focuses on human uniqueness, treating her clients like friends not patients, and putting their comfort first—but also her belief in healing and her holistic thinking. Lynette's clinical and neurofeedback applications stem from those same values and beliefs. The concepts of following the client, using neuroanatomy as guidance, using the arousal and compensatory lens, not relying on the EEG alone, putting more emphasis on behavioral symptoms, and considering who one wants to be all stem from those principles.

Regardless of how much you want to rely on data, or how much of the arousal and compensatory lens you've grasped, at the end of the day, a client is a person and not just a number. I urge you to always consider rechecking the qEEG map, to try to do things more holistically, to ask questions when analyzing your data and evaluating the behavioral symptoms, to make your client feel confident rather than broken, and to consider who your client wants to be. This sensitivity toward clients and their loved ones will provide you with effective, empowering, and endless healing. Ultimately, it's all about how we get to the top, and don't we all want to get there feeling proud and at ease about our journey? Regardless of where the field is going, let's not forget about our human complexities and differences within the science and technological worlds.

Let us remember to always reach out for tools and words that don't make our loved ones feel broken. Let's build teams that focus on healing, that see beyond the shackles of our labels, and reinforce our strengths. We should aim to respect everyone's difficulties, honor their journey, support their chosen path, and co-create a new reality for everyone. Let's make healing a mission that everyone can access.

Thanks to Lynette, many families around the world were granted that, and I hope this book inspires you to have that for yourself and those you love. I am grateful that I was able to give back to others from the generosity that my family has received. I guess that's the Lynette effect becoming the Louloua effect. Now it's your turn!

Appendix

Appendix I: Dr. Louise's Assessment Process

Appendix II: Neurofeedback FAQ

Appendix III: Full List of Neurofeedback Protocols

Dr. Louise's Assessment Process

Step 1: Check their medical history

We first inquire about their medical and brain health. We check for a history of:

- ❖ brain injury
- ❖ loss of consciousness
- ❖ concussions
- ❖ seizures

These are important since they will determine what kind of training we can expect. If the person has had a history of any of the above, we will be cautious in our protocol setup and watch closely for change and symptoms.

If there is a history of seizures, neurofeedback could potentially create one, so our protocol needs to be safe. A precautionary method is to inhibit all frequency bands.

If there is a history of brain trauma or concussion, there is a risk of pain and headaches. Those are important to treat, but there are several ways to go about it.

Step 2: Look for their self-medication or compensatory habits

To get a sense of our client's operating system and internal experience, we need to examine their self-medication and compensatory habits through categories of questions. We should inquire about their goals, diagnosis, medication, sleeping habits, moods, energy levels, clarity levels, stimulating habits, calming habits, any physical symptoms, strengths, and weaknesses.

We aim to determine the core problem, as well as the person's preferred way of being. We look for our answers in the details and the client's unfolding.

The symptoms and goals are the deciders of our prognosis. If there is a diagnosis, we use it to help guide us in what questions to ask.

We should always ask about what medication the person has taken in the past or is currently taking, and what effect it had on them, as it will provide information on how the brain reacts and what it needs. For instance, if someone likes being on SSRIs, then this shows that this person enjoys serotonin, and we might want to begin on a serotonergic pathway.

Ask the following questions:

❖ What are their goals? Struggles? Why are they here?
❖ Any known diagnosis
  ◦ Eating disorders? Anxiety? Depression? OCD? ASD? Learning disability?
❖ Medication
  ◦ What medications are they on? What have they taken in the past? For how long? How did that medication make them feel? Why did they continue or discontinue it?
❖ Sleep
  ◦ How long does it take them to fall asleep? Do they stay asleep all night? When they wake up, do they feel alert

or tired? Are they ready to start their day, or do they need their routine?

- ❖ Mood
  - ◦ Generally, do they lean more toward anger or depression?
- ❖ Energy
  - ◦ Are they generally full of energy or do they lack energy?
- ❖ Clarity
  - ◦ Do they generally have a clear mind? Or is it foggy and hard to focus? Or is there too much to think about?
- ❖ How do they help themselves to become more stimulated?
  - ◦ Do they drink coffee? If so, how much do they drink in a day? What happens if they don't drink coffee? Can they go to sleep if they've had coffee?
  - ◦ Do they crave sugar? Chocolate? Do they drink sodas?
  - ◦ Do they take or have they taken stimulants? If so, when and how much?
- ❖ How do they help themselves to calm down?
  - ◦ Do they drink alcohol? If so, when and how much?
  - ◦ Do they smoke cigarettes? Do they take depressant drugs? If yes, when and how much?
- ❖ Other self-medication/compensatory habits
  - ◦ How often do they go to the gym? What are the habits of their eating disorder? What are their OCD habits?
- ❖ Physical symptoms
  - ◦ Do they clench their jaw? Do they have hand tremors or tics? Do they get ill often? What are their bowel movements like?
- ❖ Strengths and weaknesses
  - ◦ What subjects do they perform well and badly at school or at work? Any fears?

We can get overwhelmed with all the information, so beware of oversearching and get straight to the core problem and the most desired goal. Along with determining the core problem, don't forget to figure out what it is that the person enjoys the most. Enjoying the change will reduce resistance and make healing faster while providing us with more information as the story unfolds.

For instance, if the answers show symptoms of under-arousal, you can either train at the right hemisphere, which will imply they will give in to the state (calm them) or you can train at the left hemisphere, which will imply they will fight the state (brighten them). Determining which to go for will have to do with how they enjoy being. Most of the time, 60% of what it looks like is the opposite of what it is. It's always a trial. A good place to find the answers is by looking at what happens on the way to the meltdown. What state was that person in before he became angry or depressed? We take all the information we have and make an educated guess.

Step 3: Observe and correlate their physical and psychological state with their EEG waveform and ratios

Once we have an idea of prognosis, we start training with neuro-feedback. Lynette recommends to always start in the same location. She suggests beginning the training at Cz. Since her approach is so varied, she wants us to have at least one bit of consistent data to contrast and compare with other clients. Even if it's just for ten minutes.

The client is a moving target, alive, breathing, and generating changes in the EEG.

When doing a session, we always need to be observant of the client. We ask them to take a baseline of how they are feeling before starting the session in order to properly measure any changes. We check for changes in their physical presentation and inquire about changes in their psychological state during and after the session. Are they feeling different in any way?

During the session, we observe and inquire about:

❖ the wholeness of the situation
❖ tension of the jaw
❖ tightness of the shoulders
❖ colors
❖ pupils
❖ how they are with us
❖ muscle tone
❖ clarity, energy, happiness, relaxed

While we observe their physiological and psychological changes, we also observe the EEG screen. The most important aspect to keep track of is the ratio between the selected frequency bands, not so much the numbers on their own. It's the difference between the numbers that matters because that's where the change happens. We are working on the relationship between the reward and inhibits together, not the numbers by themselves. The distance between them should change over time, but it takes repetition.

On the EEGer software, we also want to look at the spectral display and where there is a lack. A tip is to shrink the Raw EEG to about 100 to only see the obvious. Our objective is to look for patterns. We want to see little movement at the beginning with a rolling up movement and ending with a flat line. Ideally, we want to see movement, but we don't want to see high-frequency movement nor very-low-frequency movement either. All the rest should be rolling.

With the EEGer software, we can compare the subtotal to the first average at the end of the session to see the EEG changes that happened throughout the session. We can also take the reward frequency's amplitude average, multiply it by two, and compare the result to each inhibit amplitude average; if we see anything that is higher than or equal to the result, then this signals abnormality. Note that the average amplitude numbers can go as high as in the hundreds. When a seizure is occurring, the raw average can go up to 300. But high numbers indicate movement, interference, and/or dysfunction. They, like everything else, are a clue.

Step 4: Let the neurofeedback sessions give us the true answer to their arousal levels

The questions are just a start, and the information about the person now includes the therapy and the brain's response to the neurofeedback. The real answer regarding their arousal levels comes from both the EEG and the response to the sessions, and we should let the changes from neurofeedback give us more knowledge about which way we should be shifting the brain. As the person is unfolding, you learn more and see the changes happening; you can tell whether that person is going in the right direction or not. The therapist and the client work as a team, and together we discover the truth about their arousal state.

Misinterpreting symptoms due to therapeutic confusion or the individual's confusion is common; thankfully, the brain's response to neurofeedback provides clarity to the matter. Here are some examples of how neurofeedback can help uncover the truth about someone's arousal state.

Let's say we initiated a higher state of arousal in someone, thinking this person was low arousal because of his low energy, but he was actually high arousal. We invited the brain to make more high-frequency activity in the temporal lobe. However, we observed during the session that this led to even more jaw clenching than before. The muscles became tighter, and the grinding is a way to release the clamping and muscle tension. This can be rectified by reducing the reward frequencies and thus encouraging a less-aroused state. The point is that the problem and correction that occurred provided an understanding of the internal state of the client. It is important to note that this does not apply to all teeth grinders. We should heal on an individual basis and not a "one size fits all" approach.

Now let's say we meet another child with jaw tension and assume the child needs relaxing and a lower state of arousal. We go to the temporal lobes and see an indication of that in the EEG, and thus decide to reward lower frequencies and inhibit higher frequencies. However, the child ends up grinding their teeth even more. After asking the child how they are feeling, you learn they feel dizzy. Here we understand that being under-aroused led to teeth grinding for this child, as this is their way of waking up the brain to focus by increasing blood flow to the brain. Their brain has learned the correlation between biting and focus and thus has created a habitual instruction when they are feeling under-aroused. While the child isn't aware of their state or compensatory habit, we can unravel the mystery by increasing the frequency being rewarded and seeing them relax. The therapist and the client work as a team—together we discover the truth about their arousal state. We observe quickly, make decisions quickly, and make changes quickly.

When doing a session, we always need to be observant of the client. Before the session starts, ask them to take a baseline and to notice how they are feeling—how cold, hot, happy, energetic, clear they are. Then throughout the session, check in about how they're feeling and compare it to that baseline. Ask if they feel different in any way. If they aren't talking, we should look for changes physically happening in their bodies. When someone is under-stimulated, they are bathing in theta and delta waves. Their color, their muscle tone, the brightness of their eyes, their way of talking, their head position—all of these things may change. As the person unfolds, you learn more and see the changes happening and discern whether that person is going in the right direction. Ask them if they are feeling happier, less happy, or the same? More relaxed? Tired? Let's try to not to pull toward the negative and only pull toward positive placebo to truly believe in improvement.

Watch if they like you more or less, whether the relationship between you and the patient is changing. If a child, for instance, wants to pull out the electrodes right away, then it means they either didn't like the feeling they were getting from the session or they are finally feeling relaxed, which they have never felt before, so they may feel frustrated.

Continuous feedback is always needed from the patient because the EEG numbers don't stand on their own, and it's usually best to assume that any change was due to neurofeedback.

APPENDIX II

Neurofeedback FAQ

Q: Is neurofeedback addictive?

A: Neurofeedback training implies teaching the brain, and thus, as with all learning, we are changing the baseline of that person's state. Therefore, neurofeedback is not addicting because it encourages growth and change. Since we are constantly changing and recreating the baseline, there are no accompanying withdrawal effects should you stop using it. During the first sessions, it may feel as though you can't get enough and feel a need to do sessions constantly, but that's okay because we are working on changing the brain in a way that is making it healthier, stronger, and more flexible. Besides that, it is a common response to trying anything that helps us feel better. So, though we are indeed helping your brain create a feel-good chemical bath, we are also teaching it how to stay in that state and become more flexible. When you are addicted to something, you lose control. With neurofeedback, you gain control. Medicine or other forms of addiction actually cause changes in the brain wherein the brain needs the drug to function. With neurofeedback, you eventually don't need it at all. So instead of ending up stuck with your problem, you get stuck with a healthy and balanced brain.

Q: How can we compare our ratios if, from the start of the sessions, the child is moving a lot in the baseline?

A: That is why you shouldn't analyze the details in the numbers too much. In time, the children calm down, and the real numbers indicating standard deviations and true ratio differences show up. In fact, that is why we mainly look at ratios. One day it just changes, and that is usually when you see the improvements last. It's all about proportions and relationships. When the reward amplitude increases, you are also inhibiting other frequencies. This has a focusing effect on the brain, so less energy output is needed for a given task. It is like moving from a brain state of chaos to a brain state of enrichment. So, yes, watch the ratios, but don't worry too much over them in the beginning. Just use them as a guide.

Q: The client could be answering what they think you want to hear. Isn't that problematic?

A: Yes, that's why we need to look at the whole picture. At least the client is giving me her version of what she experiences. I'm most concerned about the person buying into what they say they feel, especially when they lie. Still, my job is to trust what the client said is true, and then if I see too much evidence to the contrary, ask what the incongruent details mean. It is important not to attack a person's credibility if you don't want them to attack back or shrink away. Give them an out so they can save face while admitting they lied and move from there. I want to caution you that people sometimes want the wrong thing. Still, you have to work with what they want, at least in the beginning, until you have helped them to want something else.

Q: Can neurofeedback work with something other than beeps?

A: Sound as feedback is powerful because it can reach you even if you're not looking at the computer. It leads to a quick and clean distribution of information. You can't shut your ears off the same way you can shut your eyes. The feedback is stronger if multimodal by including visual feedback as well, but information travels at different rates and to different places. So, yes, you can use vision or touch instead of beeps or tones, but I prefer the far-reaching, impactful freedom of sound. The beeps are the fastest way that doesn't require any thinking. Back in the 1970s, neurofeedback involved a written EMG device and a therapist vocally saying "yes" on the microphone whenever the electrical activity behaved the ideal way.

Q: Will other people in the room be affected by the client's beeps during the session?

A: No, because the beeps are sounded as a direct result of the changes in brain wave amplitude related to the brain with the sensor. The brains of the other people in the room may indeed check for a pattern related to their own activity, but then finding none, do what brains do, and filter out the sound. In other words, they ignore it. It's like when you hear beeps in a factory. The sound at first bothers you because your brain is trying to take control of it. But the brain will ignore it once it decides that it is not important or is out of its control. The need to ignore the beeps could create a possible hypnotic effect, similar to the way the sound of a clock ticking does, but otherwise, other people are unaffected. Truth is, everything in our environment influences us, but the brain is well equipped to focus and filter when it isn't important to its own function. The beeps aren't matching with your specific EEG, so it can't affect you. Brains make a decision about what to do with the things they encounter. That's why it's important to keep the feedback challenging because once the brain gets control and knows what to do, the performance will plateau.

Q: What exactly are you doing when you're changing the frequencies?

A: When I am changing the frequency reward from 12–15 Hz to 15–18 Hz, I am changing what I will say yes to. We are saying yes to a higher frequency group because the brain will try to make more of that frequency.

Q: What is the difference between dynamic thresholding and automatic thresholding?

A: Thresholds are what we use to set the reward and inhibits of our frequencies to provide feedback. I use automatic thresholds that are reset manually because I want to control what the home user is doing to some degree. I want to ensure that the level of difficulty is uniformly changed, but I also want the person using the equipment to have the freedom to reset at will. I designed my choices because I am overseeing people all over the world. If this were not the case, I would do it all manually because I trust my skills and prefer to always individualize treatment. Auto thresholding removes some of that individualization. On the other hand, it improves the ability to ask for a change in a uniform manner. Especially since you will be increasing and decreasing the challenge level based on how the client is doing.

As the brain resets, it's important to adapt the game level to the brain being challenged. As the client evolves during the game, it's important to move the game expectations by changing the game's percent of success in each band. The math is done by the software, so we are free to observe the client and their wave formations. In our software, the F11 button creates an across-all-bands reset move. I like that. In a way, it is good preventive medicine. All processes in the world try to move into balance. If you are asking for a change in one aspect of the brain wave behavior, everything else is also affected. I want more uniform across-band change to be made, not just that one frequency band, which is what happens with dynamic thresholding. We are working with a living organism, fully sophisticated and constantly changing, not stagnant. We need to move with it and respect its multi-layered cascade of responses. Thus, if I want to be in control of the end result, it is important to get everything to move together.

Arousal

Q: What if teeth grinding is due to a symptom related to a seizure and not to arousal levels?

A: Seizures are still a question of arousal levels. You have to start thinking as if everything is high arousal or low arousal. A seizure is a phase lock of all brain frequencies. For example, in one type of seizure, there is a focal point where the person is shooting out high amplitudes of very low-frequency brain waves. If the opposite of that location is shooting at very high frequencies, those high frequencies will grab hold of the low frequencies, and they will all fire in unison, and thus it locks. Having all frequencies fire the same is not what we want. We need diversity in frequencies and amplitudes. The brain needs to work as a baseball team. Everyone has to do their own job. The high frequencies in seizures are like a spark, and the low frequencies are like a gasoline slick. I know a seizure sounds like a high-arousal problem, but for the most part, it's a low-arousal problem. The person grinding their teeth could be trying to reduce the excess amplitude of low-frequency brain waves or be at risk of causing a high-frequency spike. The answer to which is likely found by observing the EEG and correlating that with their other behavioral symptoms. We can work on reducing the odds of a high-frequency spike or work on reducing the excess amplitude of low-frequency brain waves bathing the brain. Or we can work on both. By applying the concept of arousal and client partnering, we can also aim for optimal client comfort while treating the brain.

Q: You make it seem like self-medicating habits are bad. What's wrong with learning how to control and cope with what we have?

A: It's good and important to know how to cope, but not as good as fixing the problem. You are lucky that you can change it with neurofeedback. Life doesn't have to be so difficult, and coping shouldn't be your goal. Compensating is good, but it is also like living life on a seesaw, up then down, up then down. Too many of us think we have to have these inner wars. We learn to be incongruent and dishonest because that's the way we learned to help ourselves. But it shouldn't be that way, and we don't have to spend our lives learning how to control ourselves. Neurofeedback is better than trying to control something. If we're already busy controlling our emotions, busy controlling how we feel, and making choices, we are already using up our brain. If we don't need to, then we have more space and energy to do other things, such as help people.

Q: If someone has apraxia,[67] for example, could we still think in terms of localization and place the electrodes on the parietal lobes because that's where the problem resides?

A: When I choose frequencies, I use arousal. I also use arousal for location purposes, and I also use neuroanatomy to direct my decision, of course. If the child with the speech issue seems to understand everything really well, then I will likely not put a sensor on the receptive language area known as Wernicke, which is P6 or P7. If the problem seems to only be the ability to create the proper movements, I will likely put my sensor on Broca's area in the left hemisphere. (By the way, I hope you are noticing that I am not assuming based on diagnosis.) Now, if the child seems anxious about speech, I may choose to reward his alpha frequencies because they are less intense and may help him relax into better control of his fine motor. I'll think, "Okay, they usually do 15–18 Hz, so let's do lower and reward 12–15." So, every choice is holistic. When I'm looking for my placement, I'm thinking of where, based on behavior and neuroanatomical representation, not just arousal. Yet I always bring everything back to arousal (see figure 15).

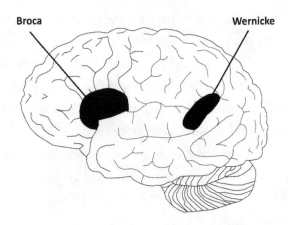

Figure 15: Figure showing Wernicke's and Broca's areas.

---

67 Acquired oral motor speech disorder affecting an individual's ability to translate conscious speech plans into motor plans, which results in limited and difficult speech ability.

Finding the Ideal Protocol

Louloua: How do I know if the protocol is the right one?

Lynette: Wherever the person was headed at the end of the session, the effect will grow bigger over the next 1–24 hours. Most typical people will feel the strongest effect in about two hours. It takes a little time for the brain to assimilate and recuperate. Other than being tired, though, they should like how they feel the whole time, though they may say it is weird to feel so different. Different people assimilate and recuperate in different ways. Some may want to take a nap, some may be hyper happy, others desire alone time. Allow them their personal style. Always wait for change: your goal is to create and watch for change. Lay what you see on the screen against what you see in their behavior. Ask parents what they want to change and listen to their answers regarding functioning challenges, sleep, mood, and medicines. Inquire into changes noticed and always monitor, before and after the session, their quality of sleep, behavior of bowels and bladder, their mood, energy, focus, and the emergence of new skills.

Unless the patient is feeling some kind of discomfort, try not to be too distracted by behaviors in the first thirty minutes after the session. That is the adjustment period. Just write down what you notice and wait for them to assimilate. Whenever possible, I try to be the one with the client so that others aren't confused by this period. After about thirty minutes, the direction of the changes should be pretty clear (more relaxed, more excited, more aware, more tired). That is when I can tell if the problem is mounting or reducing in strength. That is when I know if I need to make a change or let them go home.

Louloua: What's the difference between feelings during the session and later? Which matters most?

Lynette: During the session, it doesn't matter as much unless one is feeling nauseous or dizzy or is getting a headache. Most things are transient. It's okay to have these feelings if they're transient. When they tell you about any strange discomfort, pause the game. Now chat a little. Distract them from the feeling. If it passes, it's transient. If it doesn't, make a change in your protocol. When the brain is shifting, it is being asked to rearrange its habits very quickly. Some very sensitive people can feel that rewiring. It is much more important to pay attention to how the person feels after they have finished the session and have assimilated the changes. Give it at least twenty minutes, more if possible. You really just want to hear them tell you that they feel good. If they don't know, then ask them to compare the way they feel now to the way they felt before the session. They won't be able to answer this question if you don't ask them to notice how they felt before you started by taking a baseline of their state. (As you may recall, I always do that.) Importantly, don't panic over the weird transient things. One lady even told me her teeth felt like rocks. As long as it passes when you pause, and it doesn't come back when you resume, then it is transient. This happens especially in the beginning, probably because their brain has never done this before and is a little out of shape. It's like going to the gym for the first time and feeling every muscle. Whatever the changes, desired or undesired, give neurofeedback the credit and the blame, at least while you are trying to figure them out.

Ask questions during the session to make them feel like they're in control. It's also important to check to make sure you're not doing anything against their wishes. Simplify the questions so people can answer them. "Do you feel happier, less happy, the same? More tired, less tired, the same?"

During the session, though, you still don't have a complete picture. You want the effect to play out over the next day or two. Changes in sleep and bowels and anything physiological will be your clearest evidence for whether the session helped or not. Emotions, energy, and focus matter too, of course, but you can't worry too much about that in the first few sessions because too many life experiences and the newness of treatment elements come into play. To really get a sense of things, you need to do a few sessions so you can look for patterns of behavior. If they felt tired the first time and energized the second, but you did the same protocol, then something in their life is likely causing the difference.

Louloua: How do you track changes between sessions?

Lynette: Change is the focus of this therapy. Too often, people focus on what is staying the same. When you do that, you miss what is changing. Your client came to you for help. They do not want to stay the same. In fact, they want something specific. But because of the brain's interconnectivity, it may take a while to get there. For example, if a person wants to sleep better and that hasn't changed, you may discover that they also used to be constipated a lot and had restless legs, and these improved even though sleep didn't. Those bits of information tell you how you are affecting the client. That doesn't mean you don't go after your goal of blissful sleep. It means that those changes will help you figure out how your client operates so that you can get to your goal, and then some. To be honest, sleep usually improves before bowels and along with restless leg syndrome but not always. So, only write about change. Look for desirable and undesirable change in all categories. The categories can be specific to the person, or you can use the basic ones: bowels, energy, mood, appetite, sexual function and interest, focus, pain, body image, sensory issues related to any or all five senses, fine and gross motor challenges, worst and best subjects in school, balance, tics, stutters, problem-solving, habits, reading, writing, and speaking. Add anything the client wants to specifically target. Ask about their compensatory behavior like coffee to wake up or wine to sleep. And always ask about sleep because (like the behavior of your bowels and bladder) it is less impacted by expectation. Sleep changes are a clear indicator of arousal change when they show up. So, watch for them.

I caution you against getting too specialized in these categories. If you start thinking in terms of how his social approach behavior is improving based on if he looked at his friends when talking, for example, if you start breaking down his attention into specific categories like he stared at his homework three minutes instead of two and a half, then you will start to lose sight of the overall curve of improvement. Details are important, but they are also distracting when you worry over them too much. In my personal opinion, categorizing every little move a person makes dehumanizes them and the relationship you have with your client. It puts distance between the two of you. It's best to not break down these categories into such minute details. Look for bigger changes, and you will find them.

Louloua: How do I adjust a protocol? What is your thought process on changing protocols?

Lynette: If you trained at too high of a frequency, look for over-arousal symptoms and reverse them by training at lower frequencies or shifting the site. If you rewarded too much of a low-frequency group, look for under-arousal symptoms and reverse them by training at higher frequencies or shifting sites. For example, if you trained on the left at a high reward, and they feel nervous, train on the right at a medium reward. Make changes based on the client's feedback and by observing the client. You can balance your training time per side between the left and right hemispheres or adjust the frequencies. Once the correct frequencies and locations are figured out, we experience only improvement, alleviating symptom after symptom day upon day, and neurofeedback becomes the gift that keeps on giving.

I base it on the arousal and compensatory lens, follow the child's changes in behavior and, using his neuroanatomy as guidance, factor in the goals, and choose. Most of us gain more clarity when we think in words, so try to make a story out of all this and apply the overarching model.

Louloua: So, what do we do when we make a mistake?

Lynette: We are going to make mistakes. All clinicians do, especially if they are focused on the diagnosis rather than the symptoms. Either way, don't worry too much because even mistakes can be a good thing. This is because when you correct the mistake by doing something opposite to what you did before, you are not only correcting the error, you are also making the brain more flexible by asking it to first do one thing and then do another. The person's brain is learning not to get stuck in an emotional state but to bounce back. Remember, a flexible brain is a healthy brain, so this mistake becomes part of the healing journey. This is a wonderful therapy because whatever you do, you can undo, and if you don't know how, it's still okay because you need repeated sessions for a change to become permanent. So, all on its own, the brain will go back to where it was.

Still, let me explain again how to correct a mistake. Let's say I trained at 12–15 Hz on the right hemisphere at C4 because I assessed a client as over-aroused because he liked to drink whiskey after work. Alcohol is a depressant, so I thought he needed a protocol that would calm down his system, reduce his speed of processing. Then while I am doing the session, he gets all tensed in his face and feels uncomfortable in his body. I pause the session, but the problem continues. Now let's make the example even more challenging. Pretend the person is special needs and nonverbal, maybe around thirteen years old. Instead of drinking after work, he is stealing alcohol from his parents' cupboard. He is tense and angry with the protocol I chose. I have to fix it, but he doesn't want to continue.

I stop the session for a bit. We hang out and play. I do this to take the pressure off his need to cooperate and to regain his trust. I chat while I play and explain that I can take the tense feeling away. When he feels less resistant, I lead him back to the computer and resume the session. This time I place the sensor on the left hemisphere instead of the right. I set the reward at 15–18 Hz instead of 12–15 Hz, and voila he relaxes! You can't avoid mistakes because sometimes the correct move is counterintuitive. But you can correct what goes wrong and make it right.

If you need protocols to reverse the mistake, the rule of thumb is always to do the opposite. If you were on the right, go to the left; if you were on the back, go to the front; if you were rewarding high frequencies, shift to a lower reward. Do the opposite.

Louloua: How can I always get a change?

Lynette: Don't settle. Don't make excuses like "non-responder," and be willing to raise or lower the reward choices by more than just one or two. Make sure you look for what is improving so that you can keep those and correct for problems as they emerge. Gather information and choose your protocols fast enough to keep the client enjoying the therapy.

Louloua: How do I know that I am making changes in the long run?

Lynette: Because you see a change in the short term. They build upon each other. If you've tried many protocols and are seeing positive effects but not getting any nearer your goal, then either your goal is wrong or you need to rethink your neuroanatomy because there is a physiological problem getting in the way. You could be training a person with an undiagnosed thyroid problem, for example. Perhaps they feel tired with body aches, focus problems, and a shift in metabolism. That could be brain function in general, but it could also be hypothyroidism. We do a session on the left frontal lobe and increase stimulation there, and they'll feel better, alive, bright, happy, and energetic, but the physiological problem will drag them back. If they keep going back (or near back) to baseline, something is wrong. Because with neurofeedback, the improvements should be accumulating.

It is good to understand the trajectory of change, though. With neurofeedback, as with most mood-altering drugs, there is an obvious shift in the beginning, a honeymoon period, which eventually plateaus. With neurofeedback, the plateau indicates that the problem is corrected. With medicine, it indicates dependency and addiction. When your sessions stop having much of an effect, the need for an effect should also have dropped. That's when you either go on maintenance sessions or attack something new. To be honest, I have never seen a regression with neurofeedback. That is why I say if the person keeps going back to the baseline, physiological core problems need to be resolved. If they have a degenerative disorder like Parkinson's, then keeping them from deteriorating is, in actual fact, long-term progress.

Louloua: Where do I see the results?

Lynette: In their lived experience.

APPENDIX III

Full List of Neurofeedback Protocols

T4, alpha reward (right temporal lobe) to help with:

- calming
- understanding language
- the processing of meaning in speech and vision
- processing sound
- object and facial recognition
- detection and understanding of the emotional tone of voice and states of others
- fear responses
- decision-making

T4–P4, alpha reward (right temporal and parietal lobes) to help with:

- calming
- sensory integration
- social cues and understanding emotions
- working memory, comprehension, and attention
- verbal understanding
- combining auditory and visual information important for reading and writing

- a conscious awareness of visual-spatial events
- understanding temporal relationships
- future planning

F3, low beta reward (left frontal lobe) to help with:

- executive functions
- induction reasoning
- spatial information
- approach behavior and positive emotions
- sustaining attention
- problem-solving
- making judgments and being more sociable
- feeling brighter, happier, and clearer
- improving motivation

Cz, SMR reward (center of somatosensory and motor cortex) to help with:

- sensory integration and getting both sides of body working in concert

- control and organization of voluntary movements
- imagery, verbal encoding, and motor memory
- anticipating and understanding actions
- muscle tone, balance, and fine movement coordination
- attention and mental processing
- reducing hyperactivity
- sleep

F3–F4, low beta reward (left and right frontal lobe) to help with:

- being less impulsive
- evaluation of incoming stimuli
- planning appropriate response and inhibiting inappropriate response
- reasoning skills
- stretching one's ability to switch between states

C4–F4, low beta reward (right sensory-motor strip and frontal lobe) to help with:

- planning and initiating body movements
- inhibiting responses and behavior control
- empathy, calmness, and emotional processing
- sensory integration
- evaluating the wholeness and context of information and situations

T3–T4, alpha reward (left and right temporal lobes) to help with:

- calming
- comparing present input with past experience, organization of information
- episodic and declarative memory
- grasping the whole picture vs. auditory inputs infractions
- the "what" and "where" of auditory information
- learning disabilities
- the processing of meaning in speech and vision
- word and sentence generation
- decision-making

F4–P4, low beta reward (right frontal and parietal lobes) to help with:

- sustained attention
- abstract thinking and working memory
- understanding intentions
- self-awareness
- governing attention to and interpretation of emotional and contextual cues
- visual-spatial information
- reading, writing, and math

C3, SMR reward (left sensory-motor strip) to help with:

- planning and initiating movements
- motor sequencing, sensory guidance of movement
- rapid, alternating, and smooth sensory-motor movements that are

complex and rhythmic, imagining movements
- the processing of emotions related to reflections on self, brightening
- speech, the arrangement of words, language processing, and handwriting
- memory
- problem-solving
- homunculus for right representation in the body (arms, legs, control of the trunk, and proximal body musculature)

C5, SMR reward (left sensory-motor strip) to help with:

- vocal control and mouthing issues
- problem-solving
- planning and initiating movements, motor sequencing, sensory guidance of movement
- attention to visual actions and recognition of objects
- inhibiting responses and behavior control
- affect network
- homunculus for right representation (over the facial sensory area on the right)

C4, SMR reward (right sensory-motor strip) to help with:

- sensory integration, especially if sensory issues present all the time
- monitoring errors and topographic memories
- acoustic rhythms and melodies
- calmness, emotion, empathy

- planning, problem-solving, deductive reasoning
- memory
- planning and initiating movements, motor sequencing, sensory guidance of movement
- rapid, alternating, and smooth sensory-motor movements that are complex and rhythmic, imagining movements
- the processing of emotions related to reflections on self
- calculations
- homunculus for left representation in the body (arms, legs, control of the trunk and proximal body musculature)

C5–C6, SMR reward (left and right sensory-motor strip) to help with:

- calming facial areas that are sensory sensitive
- balancing the two brain hemispheres and feeling more connected to the body
- vocal control and mouthing issues
- drooling

C5–F3, SMR reward (left sensory-motor strip and frontal lobe) to help with:

- vocal control and mouthing issues
- problem-solving, deductive reasoning, and concrete thinking
- planning and initiating movements, language, and speech

P4, alpha reward (right parietal lobe) to help with:

- spatial position, visualization of spatial organization, perception of personal space and spatial relationships
- understanding emotions, nuances, innuendo, and gestures
- drawing and understanding of maps, attention, and working memory
- reducing hypervigilance and anxiety
- sleep
- reading, writing, and solving math
- sustained attention

Pz–Fz, low beta reward (center of frontal and parietal lobes) to help with:

- visual-spatial processing
- attention and comprehension
- pain perception and identification
- the distinction of self from other, reflections on self during decision-making
- the processing of emotions
- calm and slow OCD

P3–P4, alpha reward (left and right parietal lobes) to help with:

- sensory integration
- focus and cognitive reasoning
- auditory processing
- reading and writing
- math and algebra
- geometry and spatial relationships

F7–F8, low beta reward (left and right frontal lobes) to help with:

- repetitive talk and fixations
- spatial, visual, and auditory working memory
- sustained and selective attention
- mood and social awareness

P6–F8, beta reward (right parietal and frontal lobes) to help with:

- spatial and visual working memory
- facial recognition
- mood regulation, calming
- speech and writing
- self-awareness
- sustained attention

P5–F7, low beta reward (left parietal and frontal lobes) to help with:

- verbal expression and fluency
- visual and auditory working memory
- selective attention
- the meaning of words and verbal construction
- face-name associations and sign language
- monitoring color and shape, drawing
- attention to semantic relations and associating words with visual percepts
- reading and orthographic-phonology links

Beta Reset, beta band increment reward every 90 seconds
(parietal-occipital) to help with:

– balance
– body stillness
– calmness in the body
– spatial relationships
– social ability
– Parkinson's and Tourette's

P3, alpha reward (left parietal lobe) to help with:

– cognitive reasoning and problem-solving
– attention
– imagination and association
– spelling, handwriting, and complex grammar
– math and recall of series of numbers
– verbal comprehension
– dyslexia and algebra
– hypersensitivity or sensory defensiveness

Your task is not to seek for love, but merely to seek and find all the barriers within yourself that you have built against it.

—Rumi

About the Author

Louloua Smadi, MSc, holds a degree in neuroimaging from King's College London and received her board certification in neurofeedback from BCIA in 2016. As a neurofeedback practitioner with over six years of experience in the US, UK, France, and Lebanon, she specializes in helping people with special needs and other various brain challenges. Her passion for brain health and neurodiversity stems from her experience with her brother with autism and her own attention difficulties. She hopes to help families living with severe challenges raise the bar on what can be accomplished using brain-behavior therapies.

For more information or to explore classes and coaching in the world of caregiving, neurofeedback, and special needs, please go to www.clienttoclinician.com.

Recommended Reading

Cohen, Michael P. *Neurofeedback 101: Rewiring the Brain for ADHD, Anxiety, Depression and Beyond (without medication)*. Center for Brain Training, 2020.

Doidge, Norman. *The Brain's Way of Healing: Remarkable Discoveries and Recoveries From The Frontiers Of Neuroplasticity*. New York: Penguin Books, 2016.

Fisher, Sebern F. *Neurofeedback in the Treatment of Developmental Trauma: Calming the Fear-Driven Brain*. New York: WW Norton & Company, 2014.

Kaufman, Raun K. *Autism Breakthrough: The Groundbreaking Method That Has Helped Families All over the World*. New York: Macmillan, 2014.

Marcuse, Lara V., Madeline C. Fields, and Jiyeoun Jenna Yoo. *Rowan's Primer of EEG E-Book*. New York: Elsevier Health Sciences, 2015.

Robbins, Jim. *A Symphony in the Brain: The Evolution of the New Brain Wave Biofeedback*. New York: Grove Press, 2008.

Swingle, Paul G. *Biofeedback for the Brain: How Neurotherapy Effectively Treats Depression, ADHD, Autism, and More*. New Brunswick: Rutgers University Press, 2008.

Thompson, Michael, and Lynda Thompson. *The Neurofeedback Book: An Introduction to Basic Concepts in Applied Psychophysiology*. Wheat Ridge: Association for Applied Psychophysiology and Biofeedback, 2003.

Bibliography

"About Biofeedback." AAPB.org. Accessed December 1, 2020. https://www
.aapb.org/i4a/pages/index.cfm?pageid=3463.

Alkoby, O., et al. "Can We Predict Who Will Respond to Neurofeedback? A Review of the Inefficacy Problem and Existing Predictors for Successful EEG Neurofeedback Learning." *Neuroscience* 378 (2018): 155–64.

Arns, M. W. "Personalized Medicine in ADHD and Depression: A Quest for EEG Treatment Predictors." Dissertation, Utrecht University, 2011. Utrecht University Repository.

Betzel, Richard F., et al. "A Positive Mood, A Flexible Brain." *Brain* 139 (2016): 2104–2112.

Brown, Brené. "The power of vulnerability." TEDxHouston. June 2010. https://www.ted.com/talks/brene_brown_the_power_of_vulnerability /transcript?language=en.

Davies, Kelvin J. A. "Adaptive Homeostasis." *Molecular Aspects of Medicine* 49 (2016): 1–7.

Demos, John N. *Getting Started with EEG Neurofeedback*. New York: WW Norton & Company, 2019.

Enriquez-Geppert, Stefanie, René J. Huster, and Christoph S. Herrmann. "EEG-Neurofeedback as a Tool to Modulate Cognition and Behavior: A Review Tutorial." *Frontiers in Human Neuroscience* 11 (2017): 51.

Evans, James R., ed. *Handbook of Neurofeedback: Dynamics and Clinical Applications*. Cleveland: CRC Press, 2007.

Fiske, Donald W., and Salvatore R. Maddi. *Functions of Varied Experience*. Belmont: Dorsey Press, 1961.

Garrett, Bob, and Gerald Hough. *Brain & Behavior: An Introduction to Behavioral Neuroscience.* Thousand Oaks: Sage Publications, 2017.

Garrett, Douglas D., et al. "The Importance of Being Variable." *Journal of Neuroscience* 31, no. 12 (2011): 4496–4503.

Geissler, Julia, et al. "Hyperactivity and Sensation Seeking As Autoregulatory Attempts to Stabilize Brain Arousal in ADHD and Mania?" *ADHD Attention Deficit and Hyperactivity Disorders* 6, no. 3 (2014): 159–73.

Gratton, Caterina, et al. "Defining Individual-Specific Functional Neuroanatomy for Precision Psychiatry." *Biological Psychiatry* 88, no. 1 (2020), 28–39.

Hammond, D. Corydon, et al. "Adverse Reactions and Potential Iatrogenic Effects in Neurofeedback Training." *Journal of Neurotherapy* 4, no. 4 (2001): 57–69.

Hawkins, Jeff, and Ahmad Subutai. "Why Neurons Have Thousands Of Synapses: A Theory of Sequence Memory in Neocortex." *Frontiers in Neural Circuits* 10 (2016): 23.

Hegerl, Ulrich and C. Ulke. "Fatigue with Up- vs Down-Regulated Brain Arousal Should Not Be Confused." *Progress in Brain Research* 229 (2016): 239–54.

Hegerl, Ulrich, and Tilman Hensch. "Why Do Stimulants Not Work in Typical Depression?" *Australian & New Zealand Journal of Psychiatry* 51, no. 1 (2017): 20–22.

Hill, Robert W., and Eduardo Castro. *Healing Young Brains: The Neurofeedback Solution.* Charlottesville: Hampton Roads Publishing, 2009.

Kalin, Ned H. "The Critical Relationship between Anxiety and Depression." *The American Journal of Psychiatry.* May 1, 2020. doi.org/10.1176/appi .ajp.2020.20030305.

Leotti, Lauren A., Sheena S. Iyengar, and Kevin N. Ochsner. "Born to Choose: The Origins and Value of the Need for Control." *Trends in Cognitive Sciences* 14, no. 10 (2010): 457–63.

Li, Ting-Mei, Han-Chieh Chao, and Jianming Zhang. "Emotion Classification Based on Brain Wave: A Survey." *Human-centric Computing and Information Sciences* 9, no. 1 (2019): 42.

Louise, Lynette. *Miracles Are Made: A Real-Life Guide to Autism.* Bandon: Robert Reed Publishers, 2011.

Mattson, Mark P. "Superior Pattern Processing is the Essence of the Evolved Human Brain." *Frontiers in Neuroscience* 8, no. 8 (2014): 265.

Marzbani, H., H. R. Marateb, and M. Mansourian. "Neurofeedback: A Comprehensive Review on System Design, Methodology and Clinical Applications." *Basic and Clinical Neuroscience* 7, no. 2 (2016): 143–158.

Perkins, Amorette, et al. "Experiencing Mental Health Diagnosis: A Systematic Review of Service User, Clinician, and Carer Perspectives across Clinical Settings." *The Lancet Psychiatry* 5, no. 9 (2018): 747–764.

Pfaff, Donald W. *Brain Arousal and Information Theory: Neural and Genetic Mechanisms.* Cambridge: Harvard University Press, 2006.

Rothschild, B. *The Body Remembers, Volume 2: Revolutionizing Trauma Treatment.* New York: W.W. Norton & Company, 2017.

Sherlin, Leslie H., et al. "Neurofeedback and Basic Learning Theory: Implications for Research and Practice." *Journal of Neurotherapy* 15, no. 4 (2011): 292–304.

Teigen, Karl Halvor. "Yerkes-Dodson: A Law for All Seasons." *Theory & Psychology* 4, no. 4 (1994): 525–547.

Zentall, Sydney S., and Thomas R. Zentall. "Optimal Stimulation: A Model of Disordered Activity and Performance in Normal and Deviant Children." *Psychological Bulletin* 94, no. 3 (1983): 446.